TECHNOLOGY OF NECESSITY

Technology
of Necessity

Scientific and Engineering
Development in Israel

Roy Popkin

PRAEGER PUBLISHERS
New York • Washington • London

PRAEGER PUBLISHERS
111 Fourth Avenue, New York, N.Y. 10003, U.S.A.
5, Cromwell Place, London S.W.7, England

Published in the United States of America in 1971
by Praeger Publishers, Inc.

© 1971 by Praeger Publishers, Inc.

Library of Congress Catalog Card Number: 73–117475

Printed in the United States of America

To

SCHAI AND SAFI KOUSSEWITZKY

*who will grow up taking for granted
what Israel's scientists and engineers
have helped win for them*

Contents

Preface

The words *ein breira*, or "no alternative," have special meaning
for the story of what Israeli scientists and engineers have contributed to their people in the land of Zion and to mankind.
Science and engineering are inextricably linked to the necessities
and aspirations of the Israeli way of life. The intensive work at
the Jewish Agency's first research laboratory in the early 1900's
was put to immediate use by the inexperienced dirt farmers of
the early *aliyahs*, or waves of Jewish immigration. Their agriculture was mixed with courage and great determination. Similarly,
many of the other accomplishments detailed in this book could
not have been achieved by science and technology alone; they
also took back-breaking work by men and women with a dream
of a Jewish homeland, by people seeking safety from the pogroms
of Eastern Europe and the genocidal holocaust of Nazi Germany,
by middle-aged intellectuals with hoes in their hands, and by
young *sabras* (native-born Israelis) with national pride in their
every fiber.

My sense of this story began with a handful of anecdotes
friends told me and with my reading of W. C. Lowdermilk's
Palestine: Land of Promise (New York: Harper, 1944) and James
B. Hays's *T.V.A. on the Jordan* (Washington, D.C.: Public Affairs
Press, 1948), which projects a kind of Tennessee Valley Authority

for the Jordan Valley. Later, my own research took me the length and breadth of Israel, to laboratories in cluttered old buildings in Jerusalem, to the beautiful new campuses of the Weizmann Institute, the Hebrew University, and the Technion, and to the waterfronts of Haifa and Eilat. In the course of my visit, I met old scientists whose time in Israel began in the early 1900's and young *sabras,* both men and women, who are building the technology of the future. As I traveled from Dan to Beersheba and then some, I saw that my original collection of anecdotes was part of a fabric of dedication, devotion, and accomplishment reflected not only in the effectiveness of the Israel Defense Forces but also in the crowded Supersol grocery shelves in midtown Jerusalem.

From the time the El Al jet drops down over the Israeli coastline, swings into Lod Airport over an endless vista of citrus groves, and banks so that one can see, on the one hand, the tall buildings of Tel Aviv and, on the other, the vast factories of the Israeli aircraft industry, the story of Israeli science and technology unfolds in an unending pattern that is part Alice in Wonderland, part Old Testament, part space age, and very much belief in the centuries-old dream of a Jewish homeland.

In telling this story, I have had to be selective. Some aspects of Israeli scientific research and development are deliberately only touched upon; the research in pure science—abstract science—that is being done at the Weizmann Institute and in many of the Hebrew University and Bar Ilon University laboratories is not yet within the realm of the technology of necessity. In the same way, most Israeli medical research, although outstanding, is outside the perimeters of day-to-day needs related to national survival in an unfriendly physical environment. Much of the fascinating story of Israeli military science can be told only superficially, for a nation surrounded by self-proclaimed enemies vastly outnumbering its 2.8 million people cannot afford the luxury of security-violating braggadocio.

When I began the research for this book, I talked to Jeruhan Kafkafi, Science Adviser to the Israeli Embassy in Washington. He cautioned me to make certain I didn't give his compatriots credit for the achievements of people in other countries. He wanted me to be aware that a great deal of Israel's technological success was the result of adaptation of someone else's research to

Israeli needs. With very few exceptions, the men and women I interviewed were modest in the extreme. Each was always ready to tell me what other people had done and were doing. While there is, obviously, competition for funds among individual projects, universities, and institutes, one never gets the feeling of being caught in the kind of rivalry that creates costly competitive development (as between Lockheed and Boeing or MIT and CalTech).

Also, I found it easy to talk to Israeli scientists—even those with the most esoteric or complex interests—because they were usually much better able to relate their work to basic human needs and national problems than are many American scientists. In interviewing Israeli scientists, I rarely ran into the spate of technical jargon one hears so often in the United States. The only time my inability to speak Hebrew was a problem was when I was seeking directions from Israeli policemen. Because they are mostly from North Africa, their second language is French, which I don't speak either. English is the second language of Israeli science, a fact that has caused the Hebrew University to take strong measures to overcome the weaknesses of high school English-teaching.

Many people were helpful; to list them all would be impossible, for I formally interviewed scores of scientists and engineers, and I talked casually but purposefully with many others. Before I left for Israel, Kafkafi suggested that I make only a few advance appointments by mail from the United States, for one person would lead me to another, and so forth, and that was exactly how it worked out.

I do, however, want to express my special appreciation to the following for their time and thoughtful assistance:

Dr. Alex Keynan, Director of the Hebrew University Authority for Research and Development; Hon. Avram Harman, President of the Hebrew University; Richard Oestermann, in the University's Public Relations Office; Abner Shivitsky, Assistant to Dr. Keynan; Rosheen Ilon and Hannah Hod in Mr. Shivitsky's office; and Linda Clayman and Millie Pearlman, Hebrew University secretaries, who went far beyond the call of duty to see that I met the people I needed to see or got material I was seeking.

Also, Carl Alpert, Vice-President of the Technion; Basil Herman and David Friedlander of the Technion public relations staff; Dr. Joel Schechter, Director of the Negev Institute for Arid Zone Research; Dr. Rudolph Bloch, now a special consultant to the Institute; and Mrs. Shifra Gorin, of the Institute's Public Relations Department.

Also, Meron Medzini, Director of the Government Information Office in Jerusalem, whose knowledge of his country and ability to organize almost any kind of trip or interview are amazing; and his associates in the Government Information Offices in Beersheba, Eilat, and Tel Aviv; and M. Barkay, spokesman for the Israel Defense Ministry.

Also, Yeshuran Schiff, of Eilat-Ashkelon Pipelines, Inc.; Israel Libertovsky, Director of the Israel Shipyards; Arnold Sherman, Public Relations Director, El Al Airlines; M. Cantor, Israel's Water Commissioner; Nechemaya Myers, Public Relations Director, the Weizmann Institute; Mrs. Richard Kauffmann, who shared with me some of her husband's early papers; Carl Keren, of the National Council for Research and Development; M. Oren, of the National Sea Fisheries Laboratory; the helpful staff of the *Jerusalem Post;* and David Finn, President of Ruder and Finn, Inc., of New York and Jerusalem.

My very special thanks go to Sascha and Helen Koussewitzky, who generously shared with me their home and their vast knowledge of their country and its development, and to their son Donny, who, like his father, was always willing to guide me to places I would not otherwise have seen.

Another who deserves special thanks is my Praeger editor, Lois Decker O'Neill. Finally, a word of appreciation is due also to Patty Royster, the typist who survived a mélange of Middle Eastern names and words and technical terms in grand fashion.

This book has no bibliography, for much of its content is based on private conversations. Readers who want additional information about specific projects can get it by writing to the nearest Israeli consulate, which will forward such requests to the proper source, or by writing to the public-relations offices of the universities named.

Rockville, Maryland
December, 1970

TECHNOLOGY OF NECESSITY

I

The Israeli Way
of Doing Things

Outside the small group of buildings, scientific equipment and scraggly plant beds simmered in the desert heat and omnipresent sunshine. The temperature was about 100°—an average summer day in the Negev.

Inside, in a small office at one end of a corridor lined with cluttered laboratories, Yoel Schechter—Brooklyn-born, a graduate of the City College of New York—was settling a hypothetical argument by explaining the "Israeli way of doing things." Schechter is an Israeli scientist, now serving as Director of the Negev Institute for Arid Zone Research in Beersheba. He came to Israel to work in a *kibbutz*, served in the Jewish Brigade of the British Army in World War II, and, like so many of Israel's men of science and engineering, he now seeks solutions that are practical and meet his people's immediate needs, rather than esoteric pathways out of the laboratory or new plans that will come off the drawing boards in some dim, distant future.

The argument we were having was typical—for Israel—in that it posed two valid and highly practical sides of a basic question:

Should Israel's limited water supply be used for cattle? On the one side, a leading water engineer in Tel Aviv, who is involved in re-creating ancient irrigation methods in the middle of the desert, maintained that it was wasteful to use water to raise meat, because it takes so many thousands of gallons for each pound of beef or lamb produced. And, on the other side, a Jerusalem newspaperwoman, who had been Director of Food Rationing Publicity for the British Mandate Government of Palestine during World War II, insisted that Israel must never again be without a domestic source of protein for its population. She had lived through the food shortages of World War II, during which the British paid exorbitant prices to Arabs who brought flocks through the desert from Arabia, and she had experienced the bleak, hard years following Israel's independence, when shortages were a way of life and limited supplies of meat had to be imported, eggs were rationed, and getting enough of the right things to eat was a national problem every day.

"They are both right, and they are both wrong," Schechter said. "Neither one of them sees the real Israeli solution."

At Kibbutz Sa'ad, he explained, the members of the communal farm raise sheep. They use the sheep milk to make cheese, the lambs for meat. But sheep require natural pasture, and in the Negev the pastureland is very saline. Hence, the sheep require a lot of water.

"Suppose we give the sheep good food. Then we have to get more back from them. Well, a ewe has one lamb a year. She is pregnant five months of the year. She can be milked for about four months. The rest of the year she is strictly a user of water and food, and we get nothing back.

"But, with hormone injections, we can get two lambings a year, two seasons of milking. This means two lambs, eight months of milking, so we're getting twice as much return for our water and food investment. And that's not all—now we are experimentally growing desert bushes which require no water at all. Not far from here, you'll find a green patch of perennial bushes, some of which have lived with no rainfall for years. They are lush and green. Sheep thrive on them. This year we're going to try feeding this bush to cattle. If it works out, we're home free so far as water is concerned!"

In this brief discussion of just one problem, Schechter summed up Israel's approach to the technology of necessity: You find a solution because you have to, and you do it with what you have whenever possible. Israeli scientists have changed the sex life of the cucumber, raised salt-water fish in fresh water, found ways of making every drop of water work for them while using everything from hitherto unsuspected underground resources to the clouds above, developed their own desalination membranes, mixed apples and oranges, eliminated the use of dangerous pesticides, jammed the sound waves of the crop-destroying locust, found a simple way to remove oil pollution from fresh water, harnessed solar energy for home use, "mined" potash, bromine, and other minerals from the Dead Sea. Israeli engineers have built impossible roads and unbelievable pipelines in record time, created an aviation industry, a national water system, and a shipyard that will in the near future be turning out giant oil tankers, are nearing a breakthrough in large-scale desalination technology. Israel has its own nuclear reactor and a burgeoning atomic-energy research program.

The roots of this astonishing triumph of science and technology over a harsh and forbidding piece of geography in the Middle East were planted years before the State of Israel came into being in 1948.

Some years before Israel was created by the United Nations, Lord Peel, Chairman of a Royal British Commission established to plan the future of the Palestine Mandate territory, visited Dr. Chaim Weizmann—the Russian-born scientist and world Zionist leader who became Israel's first president, in his laboratory in Rehovot. Weizmann, whose work in organic chemistry and bacteriology was world famous (his experiments had provided the practical basis for the synthetic rubber industry), was in the middle of an experiment.

Lord Peel asked him what he was doing.

"I am creating absorptive capacity," Dr. Weizmann replied.

In those five words, Weizmann expressed the driving force that still motivates Jewish scientists and engineers. At the time, he and a handful of colleagues representing a variety of disciplines were seeking solutions to the very real problems that stood in the way of settlement of the land in Palestine. They were seeking to make it possible for *Eretz Yisrael* to absorb the descendants of a people who had scattered throughout the world in the Diaspora that followed the Roman conquests twenty centuries ago.

Subsequently, Weizmann wrote, "I feel sure that science will bring to this land both peace and a renewal of its youth, creating here the springs of a new material and spiritual life. And here I speak of science for its own sake, and applied science."

These words were written several decades after modern Jewish immigration to Palestine began, but well before the creation of Israel. From the early beginnings in the late nineteenth century, Zionist leaders and the new settlers were faced with basic problems of water supply, irrigation, soil preparation, crop viability, transportation requirements, communications, housing, human adaptability to tropical and desert conditions, and, eventually, industrial development.

Although the territory that became Israel is part of the so-called Fertile Crescent that was once the ancient world's granary, succeeding civilizations destroyed each other's sophisticated irrigation and agricultural systems. The first Jewish immigrants of the 1880's and 1890's found a land that combined potentially fertile valleys in the north with barren wastelands of desert and rocky hills and mountains. Pestilential swamps dominated much of the most fertile territory. The treeless mountains were eroded, ringed with basalt and limestone outcroppings and the crumbling remnants of ancient stone irrigation terracings. Arab agriculture was primitive at best. The few cattle to be found were grazed by nomadic Bedouin tribes. The south was a spectacular but useless, empty desert. Water was readily available only in the north.

What's more, the early immigrants faced both the intermittent and often lethal hostility of the Arabs and the intransigence and obstructionism of, first, the Turks (Palestine was part of the Ottoman Empire until the British took over under the League of Nations Mandate following World War I) and then the British.

Added to these problems was the absence of such basic resources as timber and minerals. A perennial shortage of funds for construction, irrigation projects, fertilizers, housing, and other basic essentials inhibited growth and development. The settlers often struggled along at a near starvation level.

Yet, during this era, the foundations for a modern agricultural and industrial state were set firmly into the hillsides and valleys and even in the desert. Electric power lines crisscrossed the land; farming grew and expanded. The urgencies of two major wars, which isolated Palestine from much of the world, brought some industrial development. A beginning network of roads and settlements burgeoned from the necessity for more food and the urgent requirements of defense.

In the years following World War I, the scientific and engineering research institutions that have contributed so much to Israel and the world were founded. The Hebrew University, the Technion, the Weizmann Institute, the Volcani Agricultural Research Station, the National Sea Fisheries Laboratory, and other units all had their beginnings in the 1920's and 1930's. One of the first Jewish schools established by the new immigrants was for agricultural training; it was followed shortly by a school designed to educate women for farm settlement life (probably the world's first "aggie school" for women). It is interesting to note that today about 10 per cent of the students enrolled at the Hebrew University's agricultural school in Rehovot are women, and women can be found in the laboratories and shops of almost every important research field.

In the military field, Israel's fantastic scientific development program had its beginnings in the clandestine operations of the Haganah Defense Forces, which predated the end of the British Mandate. Needed chemicals for munitions came from the Dead Sea Works, another unique Israeli scientific achievement that had its origin in the 1930's.

"Necessity" is the word that provides the key to all of these achievements. Add the word "impossible," and you have the semantic crucible in which the nation's technological successes were forged. And still are.

It might be said that Israel today is the world's most concentrated laboratory of applied science. In a space that before the Six-Day War of 1967 was less than 300 miles long and at some places only 12 miles wide, Israel represents in a microcosm almost all of the environmental and ecological problems that face developing countries in the 1970's and many of the problems that will face all of mankind in the too-long-neglected effort to reverse man-made ecological imbalances, environmental pollution, and potential food and water shortages before the end of the twentieth century.

There is probably no other country in the world where applied agricultural science has developed to such a high point. Israeli scientists do everything but psychoanalyze plants to develop strains that are disease-resistant, use little water, can be grown in off-seasons, and produce high yields. Water resource development in Israel is unparalleled from the point of view of total resource usage. The variety of desalination technologies in actual use, as well as in various stages of experimental development, is found only in the much larger United States. Water economics in Israel is more and more based on the very real but still unorthodox proposition of yield per gallon of water instead of the traditional cost-benefit approach still in force in most of the world.

Since Israel was created, industrialization has moved rapidly ahead. Israel is trying to become the Switzerland of the Middle East, a nation of small, specialized, science-based industries producing export products that will bring in money urgently needed to keep the nation economically viable. The country's universities and scientific institutions are closely linked to these developments. They help create the technology of necessity.

The need for a wide variety of crops and the potential dangers from the use of chemical pesticides, recently shown to be dangerous to human life, have led to the sophisticated use of the ecology itself in the form of biological pest control. In the citrus industry, for example, Hong Kong wasps were imported to stop the spread of damaging scale. Housing is constructed almost without wood; concrete has to withstand the special assault of the desert climate. The silvery dome of the nuclear reactor at Dimona glitters over a once barren Negev desert not far from the rolling sands on which an Italian Jew is raising Australian salt bush to feed Bedouin sheep. Not far from Dimona, new green fields and groves of trees are fed by reprocessed waste waters from the textile and chemical plants in the area and from the new city that surrounds them.

The key to Israel's technological success story lies largely within the scientists themselves. Deeply committed to the nation and the concept of a Jewish homeland, they come from all over the world. Many are men and women who fled Europe before the Nazis, bringing with them a tremendous supply of skills and knowledge. The pioneers and old-timers came as settlers or to fight in Israel's war of independence in 1948. Others are Palestine-born *sabras*. But no matter what their country of birth, they are Israelis, and this fact instills within them the motivation for innovation, adaptation, or far-out research into problems that need solving yesterday. Many switched fields, almost instantaneously, when an urgent national need took priority over what they were doing. Some have followed their original research into entirely different areas because some by-product of what they were doing proved to have greater importance.

Although each one's accomplishments are unique and important, Israeli scientists and engineers somehow seem to stay outside the ivory tower that encapsulates so many researchers in the Western world. Because so many of them have served in the Haganah, in the Israel Defense Forces, in the fields and factories of the *kibbutzim* and the *moshavem*, in the below-sea-level torpor of the Dead Sea Works and the debilitating sunlight of the Negev, they reflect a vital, realistic attitude toward the problems of their country and its people. They take a lively interest in each other's fields and share research facilities (at the Hebrew University agricultural research center, one electrode in a chicken's head "belongs" to a Hebrew University poultry scientist, the other to a colleague at the government Volcani Institute some miles away). The government's interest in scientific research—and government control over much of the purse strings—makes for coordination and cross-pollination, and keeps costly duplication to an absolute minimum.

The result is a science-based nation in which the technical achievements of the ancients are blended with the latest of today's—and sometimes parts of tomorrow's—knowledge. In fact, all of Israel seems to be a laboratory or a field station. Farmers and fishermen press the men in the laboratory or experimental farm for solutions rather than waiting for new ideas to filter down from fertilizer salesmen or by the tedious university-to-Department-of-Agriculture-to-state-or-county-agent process so familiar to the American farm scene.

Israeli scientists have made many sacrifices, both personal and economic. They are paid poorly. Ben Chorin, "the father of the Israeli poultry industry," lost two sons in the Six-Day War. Most have sons or daughters in the Army. They have worked against the combined odds of time pressures, minimal equipment and money, and the word "impossible." They get little recognition but great satisfaction.

Their results may be the desert application of a technology developed in another country or the evolution of a currently useful application of techniques developed centuries ago or, even, first reported in the Old Testament. An experimental farm in the shadow of the re-created ancient Nabbatean city of Avdot is successfully using a form of Nabbatean run-off irrigation that can be adapted by many developing countries. An Israeli engineer who once dreamed of building subways is the man who ramrodded the famous Eilat-Beersheba oil pipeline to completion in four months without a single topographical study or terrain map. (He now heads Israel's shipbuilding industry, a job he undertook at the government's request after asking a week to make up his mind so that he could scour the country to see if "there was a Jew in Israel who knows anything about shipbuilding, because I surely didn't.") Israeli fish-farming is a brilliant expansion of methods first used on a large scale in Yugoslavia.

Israeli alertness to practical application of laboratory research often leads the nation's scientists far beyond their original ideas: solar energy development creating a turbine industry; studies of kharpa-beetle control producing a possible alternative to DDT; a biogeneticist breeding a new kind of cucumber, likely eliminating one whole area of back-breaking stoop labor.

The very geographical smallness of the country, perhaps, helps bring the end result, as well as the reasons it is needed, closer to the men in the laboratory. Standing on top of the successful experimental reverse-osmosis desalination plant at the Yotvota Kibbutz in the southern Negev, engineers from the Negev Institute 125 miles to the north can see children in a swimming pool, specially designed shaded cowsheds housing bovines whose milk yield is phenomenal, an experimental farm blooming in the desert. (They can also see, quite close, the grim Jordanian mountains of Moab from which rockets are fired at the *kibbutz* and traffic on the highway below.) From the visitors' lounge at the Technion— Israel's center of applied engineering technology—high on Mount Carmel, one can see the shipyards, ocean liners in Haifa harbor, the fishing fleet, the nation's first oil refinery and only steel mill, a cement plant, and a panorama of cultivated or industrial areas stretching north to the fortresses that withstood Napoleon at Acre and later housed Jewish underground fighters imprisoned by the British. Looking behind the building you can inspect a Rube Goldberg-like apparatus testing a new kind of desalination technology—developed, incidentally, by an aeronautical engineer—and the construction site for a nuclear physics research building. (You can also see the scar where Arab guerrillas blew up a harbor oil pipeline outlet in 1969, the new gunboats recently arrived from France, and the industrially polluted Kishon River.)

What Israel's scientists and engineers have accomplished can be seen in the faces of healthy children, in new buildings going up all over the land, in thriving cities that did not exist or were just tiny villages in 1948, on the crowded shelves of the supermarkets, and in forest-fire prevention signs posted amid trees standing sixty to seventy feet high on mountainsides that were desolate rock piles not too long ago.

There are, of course, problems that are still on the "impossible" list. Many of these seem to be generic to the world at large—traffic congestion, air and water pollution, housing shortages. In these areas, Israel fully qualifies for membership in the family of fully developed nations. All four of Israel's rivers are industrially or agriculturally polluted, its major highways and city streets are impossible to drive on during the rush hour, and the air over Haifa fills the nostrils with an unlovely combination of industrial smoke, harbor smells, and oil fumes. Much effort is already being directed in these areas, but not as much as will be needed, for a small nation with a limited scientific work force has to live with competing priorities of immediate urgency. Nonetheless, it is perhaps significant that at the same time Hebrew University scientists are uncovering layer after layer of bygone civilizations under and near the Wailing Wall in the old city of Jerusalem, a veteran of the potash works and overnight construction of prefabricated stockade communities (perhaps the first prefabricated housing of modern times) in the mid-1930's is now actively engaged in urban renewal studies in "new" Jerusalem.

A native of Baltimore is devoting his time to unraveling the growing traffic problem, while road-building crews race against increasing traffic, which is compounded by mule-drawn carts, shepherds and their flocks, bicyclists, and pedestrians from countries where an automobile was rarely seen. More and more blocks of apartment houses look down on lands once peopled only by nomads or passing caravans. In 1969, Israel had to import cement, for demand finally outstripped the indigenous supply.

The economics of Israeli technology is difficult at best. The national budget is beset by the costly priority of defense spending. Also, a good deal of Israeli research is financed from abroad; it is estimated that Israel does more health research for U.S. Government agencies than any other nation and is second only to Great Britain in research contracted for by U.S. defense agencies. Unfortunately, the U.S. Government as a fund resource is drying up: hence, the crash program to develop science-based industries, which will soon eclipse agriculture as the basic *economic* factor in Israel and, as a result, could sharply alter the way of life in a nation that has its roots in a worldwide Jewish return to the land.

Such problems notwithstanding, the technology of necessity will undoubtedly prevail in Israel unless world politics and Arab enmity lead to another Diaspora. One hopes and believes this outcome is unlikely, for a nation whose scientists can find a harmless way to sop up oil flowing into the water supply from a sabotaged pipeline (at the same time Santa Barbara, California, clean-up crews struggled with harmful detergents), can grow luscious fruits and vegetables in a waterless desert, and can create productive lives for a population that has tripled in two decades, has much to offer not only its own people but the whole world.

II

In the Beginning, There Was Practically Nothing

Scientific and technical development in Israel cannot be taken out of the context of what has gone before. The work done in Israel's laboratories, experimental farms, research institutes, and industries is, in the realest possible sense, an extension of Jewish history in Palestine. The need for water today is just as great as it was thousands of years ago, when the children of Israel confronted Moses in the ugly, barren, superheated Wilderness of Zin and demanded that he assuage their thirst and that of their flocks. Israel's technology of necessity is a continuum, stretching from the days of the ancients (interrupted, of course, by the Babylonian and the Roman conquests that created the Diaspora and spread Palestine's Jews throughout Europe and North Africa) with Moses, Joshua, Noah, Solomon, and other Old Testament leaders at one end and their twentieth-century counterparts at the other.

By the time Moses led his people out of Egypt into the Promised Land, many civilizations and cultures had already come and gone in the part of the world that came to be known as Palestine. Divine intervention—in the form of what modern scientists believe was a tornadic storm—raised the Biblical pillar of salt, delayed the pursuing Pharaoh and his soldiers, and then parted the waters of the Red Sea long enough to let the Israelites cross over safely to the Sinai. Taking a circuitous route to avoid the well-armed Edomites and Moabites, Moses and his followers wandered eventually into the Wilderness of Zin.

Except for the existence of power lines, scattered border posts, a concrete highway, and an occasional highway sign or "Irish bridge" (a marked dip in the road where a flash flood might sweep down through a wadi and submerge the road or wash out a true bridge), the Wilderness of Zin today looks very much as it must have to the parched people of the Exodus. Well below sea level at the lower end of the Dead Sea, it is a lunaresque landscape of striking colors and strange rock formations, eroded cliffs, and mounds of eons-old chemical or soil deposits, which surround a rolling desert marked only by occasional patches of indigenous plant life. For Moses and his band, who had left behind the lush, fertile farmlands of the Nile delta, this desolate wilderness rising from the salt marshes of the Dead Sea toward the mountains of the central Negev must have been a forbidding sight indeed.

The Book of Numbers (20:2–5) says:

> Now there was no water for the congregation; and they assembled themselves together against Moses and against Aaron. And the people contended with Moses, and said, "Would that we had died when our brethren died before the Lord! Why have you brought the assembly of the Lord into this wilderness, that we should die here, both we and our cattle? And why have you made us come up out of Egypt, to bring us to this evil place? It is no place for grain, or figs, or vines, or pomegranates; and there is no water to drink."

Fortunately, the Lord again intervened, giving Moses a capability that modern groundwater seekers would like to have. He "lifted up his hand and struck the rock with his rod twice; and water came forth abundantly, and the congregation drank, and their cattle" (Numbers 20:11). And at Marah—the Hebrew word for bitter—when the well water proved to be too brackish to drink, the Lord instructed Moses to sweeten the water by throwing a tree into the well. It worked. Today's Israeli scientists would

like to know how and why it worked, for they must turn to much
more complex and costly desalination technologies to accomplish
the same result.

The Bible and the Talmud refer frequently to agricultural problems. Much of ancient Jewish law deals with such practicalities
as boundaries, crop rotation and disposal, the care and distribution of domestic animals. The Bible contains prayers for rain and
for the fertility of cattle. Moshe Prywes, in his book *Medical and
Biological Research in Israel* (New York: Grune, 1960), comments that

> . . . many of the problems which vexed the ancients are still actual
> today, for climate, terrain and plant and animal life have changed
> little during the centuries, apart from the erosion of extensive areas
> in the hills and deforestation, and the extermination of some of the
> ancient fauna, e.g., the lion, bear, wild ass, ostrich, etc.

To some extent, also, the Old Testament is a nonspecific chron-
icle of great feats of engineering and technology. In Genesis
(4:22), the statement "And Zillah . . . bore Tubalcain, an instruc-
tor of every artificer in copper and iron" indicates that Tubalcain,
at least, had a well-developed knowledge of how to work with
metals. Actually, there were some small iron deposits in one part
of ancient Palestine, but the only major source of metallic ores
were King Solomon's copper mines in the Wadi Arava near
Timna. Solomon built his smelters at the Judean seaport of Ezion-
Geber, not far from where the Israeli Red Sea port of Eilat is
today. His smelters functioned somewhat along the lines of the
Bessemer process used in modern steel mills. Until the mines and
smelters were fully developed, all metals had to be imported,
hence the necessity for David to go up against Goliath using
readily available flinty pebbles and his slingshot, while the Philis-
tines were armed with iron and bronze. (In 1948, the home-made
Davidka routed the better-armed Arabs at Safed.) The Old
Testament tells, too, of the building of the Tower of Babel, the
Sanctuary in the Wilderness, and Solomon's Palace, all major
achievements of architectural engineering. In a rare bit of detail,
it gives Solomon credit for accomplishing what today's anti–noise-
pollution engineers would like to do: "And the temple when it

was in building was built of stone made ready before it was brought thither; so that there was neither hammer nor axe nor any tool of iron heard in the Temple while it was in building" (Kings 6:7). The excavations now being carried on around the Wailing Wall in Jerusalem—all that remained above ground of the Second Temple after it was sacked by the Romans—have uncovered signs of astonishing architectural and engineering knowhow.

Today, the tourist in the Old City of Jerusalem can walk in water up to his knees through another remarkable example of ancient Jewish engineering capability, the Siloam tunnel, which brought water, through solid bedrock, into the walled city. The entrance is down a few stone steps, through pools of water standing in an enclosure below the Dung Gate to the Old City. The tunnel goes through solid limestone into the darkness under the old Jewish quarter. It twists and turns, and the water is cold in the dark. According to the Bible, the tunnel was hewn in the rock to bring water into the original Jerusalem, which had no natural water supply, but the Bible says only that King Hezekiah "made a pool and conduit and brought water into the city" (II Kings 20:20), and that "he stopped the upper course of the Gihon and brought it straight down to the west side of the city of David" (II Chronicles 32:30). In 1882, an inscription hewn in stone by workmen who dug the water tunnel was discovered near the old conduit. It tells how the ancient sandhogs started from opposite directions, and with great engineering skill managed to meet. The inscription recounts the moment when "there were only three cubits more to cut through [and] the men were heard calling from one side to the other" and says that "on the day of the piercing the workmen struck to meet the other, pickaxe against pickaxe, and there flowed the waters from the spring to the pool for a space of 200 cubits." A modern version of the ancient sandhogs' excitement may be found in descriptions of the tunnel-building that was part of Israel's National Water Carrier construction in the 1950's. Just as the tunnel of Siloam was a survival lifeline for the city of David, so, too, the tunnels and canals of the eighty-mile-long Carrier became a lifeline for another Jewish nation.

There are many interesting examples of applied technology

among the ancient Jews, not the least of which are the findings of Dr. Jacob Feld, a New York consulting engineer who specializes in structural problems. In 1931, Feld joined British military engineers in a study of the walls of Jericho. Fifty feet below the surface, they found shards dating to Joshua's time that "definitely showed a man-made failure." But, Feld concluded, it was knowledge of soil mechanics rather than the blowing of horns that brought down the walls. Feld's theory is that Joshua had calculated correctly that his sappers with picks and shovels could undermine the walls in the soft Jericho soil, and could do it within the six days mentioned in the Bible, for the foundations of that era were rarely more than five feet below the surface. The rams' horn–blowing priests were, Feld believes, a psychological warfare diversion rather than the agents of the wall's destruction.

All this is Old Testament history. Later, the agricultural and irrigation systems of the Jews were expanded by the Romans. The Nabbateans developed a thriving agricultural and trading civilization in the Negev, where, it is believed, more than 100,000 people lived fruitfully in what later reverted to spectacular but barren wasteland. In the centuries following the expulsion of the Jews and the fall of the last Jewish fortress at Masada 2,000 years ago, Palestine was conquered by the Arabs, the Seljuks, the Crusaders, the Ayyubids, the Mamelukes, and finally, in 1517, the Turks. But small Jewish agricultural communities persisted in the Upper Galilee at least into the Middle Ages, and a tiny group of Jewish farmers existed in the village of Pekiin, northwest of Safed, until 1936.

There is a unique sense of continuity in the Holy Land. Standing on the top of Mount Scopus and watching the sun set behind the domes and spires and TV antennae of Old and New Jerusalem, one can almost hear the sounds of an ancient shepherd and his flocks who probably stood at the same spot and watched a similar sunset thousands of years earlier. Not surprisingly, the application of science and technology to the early settlement of what became the modern State of Israel in many respects reflects this continuity. Wild wheat and barley and oats dating back to Biblical times were rediscovered and grown for their centuries-old qualities of resistance to rust and other blights. King Solomon's mines were found and are being expanded. Ancient irrigation systems were revived, Biblical cures incorporated into a modern pharmaceutical industry, hills and valleys restored to their earlier productivity.

The Jewish return to Palestine began in a very small way in the mid-sixteenth century with the expulsion of the Sephardic Jews during the Spanish Inquisition. They settled in the ancient city of Tiberias. In the following century, Cossack pogroms resulted in another influx, this time from Eastern Europe, but it was not until the nineteenth century that Jews began to arrive from many parts of the world. By 1880, there were about 24,000 Jews in Palestine, living largely in Jerusalem, Tiberias, Safed, and Hebron, all considered holy cities. These early settlers were not interested in agricultural development but rather in a purely religious life. Their income derived largely from charitable collections made in Jewish communities around the world.

It was in the 1830's that the first attempts at agricultural settlement began, but they did not become realities until late in the century. In 1870, the Alliance Israélite Française founded the Mikveh Yisrael Agricultural School near Jaffa to train young Jews in Palestine to become farmers; this was the first such Jewish institution in Palestine since a technical school at nearby Yavne was closed down during Roman times. In 1878, the first agricultural settlement was created on a large stretch of land north of Jaffa. The settlers fought valiantly against malaria and Arab opposition, but the settlement, at Petah Tikvah—which means "Gate of Hope"—failed. When the first Zionist immigrants came to Palestine to begin the building of *Eretz Yisrael*, the Jewish homeland, in the 1880's, they found only 24,000 urban Jews and an agricultural school.

The Chovevi Zion (Lovers of Zion), fleeing the 1881 pogroms in Eastern Europe, became the first Jewish equivalents of the American "sodbusters" and cattlemen who opened up the Western United States to large-scale settlement. But, contrary to popular concept, these early immigrants did not set about "making the desert bloom." The development of the arid deserts of the Negev did not begin in earnest until the middle 1940's and then was undertaken primarily for defensive purposes. The early settlers moved largely into the northern coastal regions and the Jezreel Valley, then spread through the Galilee and the Jordan Valley. Rather than turning deserts green, theirs was a mission to reclaim the unworked and often swampy fertile soils and the denuded, rocky hillsides that had become bare through centuries, during which trees were cut down for fuel, stone terraces had fallen apart, and erosion had washed away much, if not all, of the soil cover.

The first immigrants were not farmers. Coming from towns and cities, their knowledge of agriculture was extremely limited. What little they knew about farming stemmed from their observing peasants working the land in Eastern and southeastern Europe. To them, raising grain in good, flat, black soil was the essence of successful farming. Such soil was readily available on the coastal plain and the southern edge of the Hula Valley. It was only after a year or two of struggle that they found the land had been left undeveloped by the Arabs because it was marshy and malarial. The early settlers at Petah Tikvah, Rosh Pina, Rishon Letzion, Hadera, Ness Ziona, and Yesod Ham'ala suffered terribly from malaria and were ready to give up when Baron Edmund de Rothschild sent French experts in to see what could be done. He imported eucalyptus seedlings from Australia, with their tremendous water consumption, to dry up the swamps, and had drainage ditches engineered and dug to drain swamp waters into the Mediterranean. His agronomists suggested that the farms be modeled on those in Southern France rather than those of Eastern Europe. Viticulture replaced grain farming, and vineyards and orchards sprang up on the reclaimed land. Such farms could also be established on the lighter red "hamra" sands of the coastal strip. They were irrigated with water from wells sunk into the soft soil to tap the large supply of groundwater, which had not hitherto been used for farming in that part of the world. Unfortunately, as it turned out, these farms depended too much on outside markets for their income and did not provide food for the increasing number of Jewish settlers.

When the First Zionist Congress met in 1897 in Basel, Switzerland, the new Palestine was fifteen years old. There were now eighteen Jewish settlements, but only Rehovot and one or two

and Deganya, the tree-planters at Hulda and Ben Shemen, and struggling farmers at other settlements were pioneering the return to the land for tens of thousands of Jews yet to come, Jewish scientists were beginning to build the foundations for agricultural research that would eventually make their nation able to feed itself and would bring Israeli produce to the markets of the world.

One of these men was Aaron Aaronsohn, a young scientist who had grown up at Zichron Ya'acov, near Haifa. A self-taught botanist, agronomist, and geologist, he had traveled the Negev between 1904 and 1908, seeking out agricultural possibilities, had laid the groundwork for Blanckenhorn's first geological map of Palestine and for other people's books on the plants of Israel. His constant goal was to find ways to restore the fertility of Palestine's arid soils. He believed that there were ancient techniques of dry farming that could be applied by the new immigrants.

Aaronsohn gained world fame with his discovery of the original wild wheat. Like other grains, wheat plants become weaker and less disease resistant over the centuries. If wild wheat in its original form could be found, cross-breeding it with cultivated wheat could produce hardier species, he believed. He was encouraged in his search by Warburg, whom he met while studying in Germany in 1902. For three years, Aaronsohn scoured the countryside looking for some ordinary-appearing grass that might have evolved into present-day wheat. Finally, he began to look for grasses so similar to cultivated wheat that they would be hard to distinguish as different. It was then that he noticed "wheat growing wild in the crevices of rocks, and the remarkable thing was that this wild wheat had heads as large as the cultivated wheat of California, for instance."

Subsequently, Aaronsohn went to the United States to address groups of farmers, botanists, and foresters and to do special work for the U.S. Department of Agriculture. Of this trip, a writer in the *Chicago Jewish Forum* (Summer, 1954) said that "the vigorous, ruddy-faced, blue-eyed young man from the mountain village of Zichron took America by storm." Among his admirers was President Theodore Roosevelt. "Spellbound, for a full hour the great man listened to Aaronsohn's account of his explorations and their relation to American agriculture. It was said that this was one of the rare occasions that Roosevelt listened to anyone so long without interrupting."

When he returned to Palestine in 1910, Aaronsohn had financial backing to set up an agricultural experimental station at Athlit, a Crusader stronghold known for its sterile soil and surrounded by the same salt fields that today produce most of Israel's salt. He chose the site to prove that there was really no such thing as worn-out or sterile soil. Using the same implements as the Arabs but plowing better and harrowing oftener, Aaronsohn applied dry-farming methods to the apparently useless soil. The resulting yields were astonishing: six and one-half times as much wheat as on neighboring farms, four times as much barley, and twenty-three and one-half times as much oats, and all this without any fertilizers.

Before his experiments could be put to use in the Jewish settlements, World War I broke out, bringing extreme suppression of the Jewish colonists by the Turks. The Jewish settlements and all Jewish enterprise in Palestine came close to being wiped out (they were saved from total extinction only by the intervention of the German Government, which was allied with the Turks, and by the U.S. Ambassador to Turkey, Hans Morgenthau). Aaronsohn, believing that only a quick Allied victory would save the situation and that the future of Jewish development in Palestine rested with the British, organized a small but extremely effective intelligence group to work behind the Turkish lines in the Middle East. On one occasion, in the Negev, he asked a British officer why water for the Army was being trucked in from Egypt when it could be found just 300 feet below the surface where they stood. To the incredulous officer, he explained that both the rock formations in the area and the writings of Josephus Flavius, the chronicler of ancient times in the Holy Land, were evidence enough. Pipes were sunk, and the water was found. (It is a fascinating sidelight that Aaronsohn, while leading an anti-Turkish spy group, was put in charge of the Turkish Government's fight against a locust invasion in 1915, which he undertook in a vain effort to save Jewish crops.)

Tragically, Aaronsohn died shortly after the war, when his plane crashed while he was flying from London to Paris in connection with political activities surrounding the Balfour Declaration, which enunciated for the first time the principle of the Jewish homeland.

Another young agronomist who left his mark on Israeli agriculture was Itzhak Wilkansky, today known as Professor El'azary Volcani, who later headed the Hebrew University's School of Agriculture and after whom the Israeli Government's Agricultural Institute at Bet Dagan is named.

Wilkansky had been a teacher at the agricultural school started in the early 1900's at Ben Shemen and had managed the afforestation project at Hulda before being named manager of Ben Shemen. A strong Zionist raised in a traditional Russian Jewish family, Wilkansky studied agriculture because he believed that in this field he could best help in the growth of Jewish Palestine, and his work in the agricultural field was always interwoven with his convictions about the ways in which Jewish settlement should be promoted. Wilkansky's special expertise was in the area of applied agronomy. He advocated crops that, insofar as possible, could be mechanically sown, and intensive research and experimentation to develop optimum farming for all of the country's widely varied soils and climates. Wilkansky spread his work beyond the Herzl forest, using the open spaces between the young saplings for experiments in cereal crops. He found ways of lightening the heavy soil at Hulda and Ben Shemen and produced there the finest wheat in the land. Capitalizing on the experience of German vegetable-, forage-crop-, and dairy-farmers in a nearby colony, he planted experimental crops and used artificial fertilizers to develop the best high-yield crop rotation schemes for varied soils. He undertook the first large-scale cattle-breeding experiments, crossing the climate-resistant Arab cows with high-yield Friesian and Dutch cows, with results that have had a far-reaching influence on dairy farming in Palestine. He began poultry farming experiments that proved white Leghorns the chickens most suitable to the climate of the Holy Land. He turned Ben Shemen into a training farm to teach modern agricultural methods.

The work done by Aaronsohn, Wilkansky, and other agronomists, geologists, and engineers during this early period was as much socio-economic as it was scientific, for it was done within the context of the Zionist movement's efforts to determine the patterns of settlement that would best enable Jews returning to the land to make a social and economic success of that return. Turkish laws and the intransigence of Turkish officialdom often demanded that land had to be settled and cultivated within stated periods lest it be up for grabs by Arab squatters. There were problems of markets for the produce, and the need for jobs for those immigrants who had to settle in the towns and cities until agricultural land was available and for part-time work to support the farmers whose farms were not economically self-sustaining. And there was the perennial problem of money shortages. Funds from Zionist organizations in other parts of the world were usually far from adequate for the purchase of enough land and equipment or for the cost of providing adequate housing for the workers in the settlements. It was a period of experimental, hazardous pioneering in which different types of settlements—the communal *kibbutz*, the cooperative *moshav*, and private land-holdings—all had their beginnings in trial and error. One important factor governing the direction of early agricultural technology was the problem of how much land to allocate to each settler or family, and this related in large measure to what could be grown under what circumstances.

Interestingly, the settlement at Ben Shemen also seems to have set a pattern for future community development that goes far beyond farming per se. When the settlement was being formed, twenty-five of the acres were sold to a company founded by Russian Zionists to build a factory to process oil from the olives that would be grown there, thirty acres were set aside for housing for the workers, and another plot was sold to Israel Belkind, an early pioneer who had been a founder of Rishon Letzion, to establish an agricultural school. (Since 1948, large cities have been created that are, in effect, large-scale versions of the original Ben Shemen pattern.)

The factory was the brain-child of another of Israel's early technologists of necessity, Nahum Wilbush, a Russian engineer who, in 1903, had emigrated to Palestine—then a country that was the most backward part of the Turkish Empire from the point of view of industrialization. The Turks forbade the use of electricity, and there were only a few steam engines being used in the country. The Jaffa orange groves and the flour mills used oil motors. Water-powered flour mills operated only during the winter when there was enough river flow to turn the millstones. Olive oil was primitively produced by small presses in the villages.

Arab artisans wove cloth in Migdal, near Gaza, and in Gaza and Ramle, ceramic household utensils were baked from local clay. In Hebron, glass was blown from scraps, and, in Acre, the Arabs made copper utensils. In Jerusalem and Bethlehem, the Christians made souvenirs and religious articles. Probably the largest manufactured items were the lighters made locally in Jaffa for off-loading ships coming into what was then Palestine's only major seaport. The only export industry of any size was the Nablus soap factory.

Outside of Haifa, then a small town of about 7,000 with only a handful of Jews, a colony of German Templars who had come to the area in 1862 had built a thriving, highly mechanized agricultural and industrial community. They had good farms, factories to make machines, tiles, macaroni, mail-coaches, and soap. Notwithstanding this example of what could be done, the Zionist leadership ignored industrial possibilities. They believed industry to be purely the province of private enterprise, and considered themselves engaged in a community resettlement bound firmly to the land and to agriculture. (In 1888, when Joseph Navon of Jerusalem was granted the concession to build the Jaffa-Jerusalem railroad, he could find no Jews to organize and carry out the project. It was turned over to a group of French Christians. The first Jewish factory had been built by Leon Stein in 1892, at Jaffa, to produce mechanical equipment for Jewish and Arab orange groves. A foundry was added so that parts could be made of cast iron. But, in 1908, the Anglo-Palestine Bank, founded by the Zionists, felt the firm's debts were too great and called in the loan. In addition, the Zionist bank manager did not believe public money should be used to support private industry. The plant was closed down.)

Wilbush came to Palestine from Minsk, after completing studies at the Polytechnic School and a special course in industrial management. He made a horseback survey of industrial opportunities that took him from the Dead Sea to Damascus. Returning to Minsk, he met with a group of Russian Zionists to organize a company for industrial development in Palestine. The first project was the construction of the olive oil extract plant in Ben Shemen. Before it was built, the Russian engineer worked as a foreman in a similar plant in Brno in order to gain practical experience.

A year later, after the Ben Shemen plant was successfully producing olive oil at a profit, Wilbush and a friend, Samuel Pevsner, built another factory in Haifa, which was rapidly developing as a seaport and rail center, to extract oil and make soap. Within two years, they added a machine factory and brought together the leading skilled workers and professionals then in the country— soap-maker Nahum Ehrman, cast-iron foundry expert Nahum Greenspan, boilermaker Joseph Orlow, and engineers Tovia Dounci and Baruch Katinka. Because Theodore Herzl had viewed Haifa as Palestine's industrial city of the future, the name chosen for the factories was "Athid," the Hebrew word for the future. It was prophetic. Industrial engineer Nahum Wilbush's Athid factories soon employed 100 Jewish workers and sparked the growth of the Jewish community in Haifa.

III

Organized Pioneering

During the period following World War I, scientific and technical development kept pace with, and sometimes led, the growth of Jewish settlement in Palestine. But, because this growth was inextricably linked with the problems of the Zionist movement, which faced British and Arab intransigence during this era of the British Mandate, nothing in the way of technological advance happened for its own sake. The pioneering agronomists, engineers, water-seekers, and others were putting their skills to work not in a laboratory vacuum but for a cause and for a people in whom they believed.

It is difficult to single out those who made the most important contributions, but Itzhak Wilkansky's agricultural research continued to expand, and he was joined in other fields by Leo Picard, a young geologist who came to "find water for my people"; Pinhas Rutenberg, who was determined to electrify the area; and Moshe Novemeysky, who applied techniques learned in frozen Siberia to the extraction of minerals from the subtropical Dead Sea. Architect Richard Kauffmann introduced the first completely planned communities and designed prefabricated tower and stockade settlements, which were constructed overnight for security purposes. The Hadassah Women's Zionist Organization initiated vital public health services in Palestine. This period also saw the birth of Israel's first great scientific and engineering schools and research institutes.

Rutenberg's electrification projects had a particularly profound impact, because they opened the way for large-scale irrigation and industrial growth. Born in the same Russian village as the Deganya settlers, Rutenberg trained as an engineer and worked in Russia's biggest steel factory until the 1905 uprisings, after which he moved to Italy and studied hydrological technology and designed large dams that could be built inexpensively. While in Italy, Rutenberg turned to Zionism and became interested in the possibilities of hydroelectric development in Palestine. According to a Palestine newspaper account at the time of his death, as early as 1915 he wrote, "As an engineer, I have not the least doubt that the sands and deserts of Palestine can and will be turned into fertile farmland; that its waterways are a potential source of tremendous industrial energy. Because of this and because of its geographical situation, Palestine is destined to become a center of world trade and will be able to support a population of many millions."

On a hot summer day in 1919, finally arriving at Deganya, the engineer announced: "I'm Pinhas Rutenberg. I want to bring electricity to this country." He rented a horse, and set out on a three-day survey of the area. His dream was to build a hydroelectric dam at the confluence of the Jordan and Yarmuk rivers below Lake Tiberias.

His request for the concession to build an electric power system met considerable opposition in the British Parliament and from Arab extremists but was finally granted in 1921. While waiting for it to be awarded, Rutenberg obtained contracts for roadbuilding in Tiberias, providing jobs and heavy-duty construction experience for hundreds of unemployed immigrants. The Rutenberg plan was to base a national electric system on powerhouses in Tel Aviv, Haifa, and on the Jordan. The first was completed in Tel Aviv in 1923, and, when the lights came on for the first time, cheering crowds carried Rutenberg on their shoulders to a *café* for celebrations and toasts to the future of electric power in

Palestine. By July of that year, all of Tel Aviv had electricity; the Tiberias and Haifa powerhouses began generating power in 1925. (Years later, Chaim Weizmann said Rutenberg had done more to build modern Palestine than any other single person except Baron Rothschild, the founder of the modern settlements.)

Meanwhile, preliminary work began on the Jordan plant at Naharayim, which means "twin rivers." The flow of the Jordan was reversed and the Yarmuk diverted as tunnels and cofferdams were built. Lake Tiberias became a reservoir to provide continual water for the turbines. Visitors to the site found workers living in houses provided by Rutenberg, who even bought them a piano so that the musically talented could play classical music after work. Asked if he had any problems with his workers, Rutenberg commented only that the men had demanded a full explanation of the project before they would start work, a typical Israeli attitude. Visitors also found signs with the names of all the tools and instruments written in Hebrew, hitherto a language believed unsuited to technology.

Construction was designed to capitalize on the 150-foot difference between the height of Lake Tiberias and the Jordan and to use dams and tunnels to divert the Yarmuk and bring the Jordan through a mile-long tunnel to a lake created by the dammed-up Yarmuk. The combined waters would flow through another tunnel, dropping seventy-two feet through generator turbines before rejoining the Jordan below Deganya. When the dam was completed, the Yarmuk no longer flowed into the Jordan. The Jordan flowed into the Yarmuk. Twice the work was delayed by floods, but by mid-1931 everything was ready for testing. Just a few technicians were there when the floodgates were opened and the turbines began turning. The company's annual report for that year says the single hydroelectric operation supplied enough power to handle the full load then being demanded of Palestine Electric.

By 1947, when the Arabs occupied the power station, Palestine Electric had over 124,000 customers and was generating close to 300 million kilowatts annually. During that year, extension of lines to Jerusalem was stopped by the fighting, the Tel Aviv powerhouse was bombed, and the workers at Naharayim were interned. Seven power company employees were killed while on duty. Until the Arab Legion destroyed most of it in 1948, the plant stood as a unique symbol of Western scientific development. All that's left now are some sluiceways that were closest to Israeli territory, separated from passers-by by lush fields of the border *kibbutzim* and hidden Israeli artillery posts.

Rutenberg died in 1942, without knowing what war was to destroy—or that the rest of the system he pioneered would eventually carry the company's full power load without the dams at Naharayim. Twenty years after the plant's destruction, a greatly enlarged Israel Electric Corporation sold more than 4 billion kilowatt hours of electric power. One-fourth of this load was used for water-pumping, one-third for industry, living proof that Rutenberg was a realistic prophet.

Moshe Novemeysky was another Russian-born engineer whose dreams turned into reality and became a foundation for Israel's future chemical and fertilizer industries. Born to a family of political exiles in Siberia, he got his engineering education in Irkutsk, did postgraduate work in Germany, and worked in the Lena gold fields and in German lead, zinc, copper, and potash mines and refineries. In Siberia, Novemeysky extracted salts and minerals from frozen lake sludge, thus beginning the career that would later be of such benefit to the Israelis living in subtropical heat. In one of his autobiographies, *My Siberian Life* (London: Max Parrish, 1956), he wrote:

> Curious to relate; the successful results of a method of extraction by freezing out at low temperatures . . . provided me years later with a key to understanding the analysis of the water of the Dead Sea in Palestine, so that I was able to establish the hypothesis of the feasibility of applying the same process in the hot climate of the Dead Sea, there making use of the high local temperatures for purposes of evaporation.

Like Rutenberg, Novemeysky had trouble during the abortive 1905 Russian revolution and the pogroms that followed. He went to Berlin and became interested in Zionist plans for Palestine. In the Palestine Bureau library, he read confidential geological reports, one of which contained a detailed description of the Dead Sea.

Only 12,000 years old—the youngest major body of water on earth—the fifty-mile-long Dead Sea fills the deepest continental depression in the world. Its surface is about a quarter-mile below sea level. At its widest, in the north, it is eleven miles across. A tongue of land, the Lashon Peninsula, divides the Sea. The larger northern basin is over 1,250 feet deep; the southern part averages only twenty feet in depth. It is fed by the Jordan River and by floods and streams coming down through wadis and canyons cut into rock walls of Nubian sandstone. On one side, near the Dead Sea Works, is Mount Sdom, the salt mountain whose eroded columns are said to include the one into which Lot's wife was turned. Called at times the Asphalt Sea, because occasional blocks of that substance rise to the surface after being exuded from underwater springs, and at times the Salt Sea, the Dead Sea was used by the Egyptians as a source of asphalt for caulking ships and wrapping mummies and by others as a source of salt. Crumbling ruins of Roman forts still guard the long-unused caravan routes over which the salt was carried, looking down today on heavy-duty trucks hauling potash and bromine from the modern plants at Sdom.

The Dead Sea has the highest salt content in the world; every litre of water contains 12 grams of potash and 4.5 grams of bromine. It contains an almost inexhaustible supply of important dissolved salts: 22 billion tons of magnesium chloride, 11 billion tons of sodium chloride, 6 billion tons of calcium chloride, 2 billion tons of potassium chloride, 980 million tons of magnesium bromide, and 200 million tons of gypsum.

The reports in the Warburg library in Berlin inspired in Novemeysky the concept of using solar evaporation to extract Dead Sea minerals. In 1911, he made his first trip to Palestine, and, ignoring warnings against Arab brigands and the terrible heat, he took a cab to Jericho and then rode horseback to the northern end of the Dead Sea. Although used to the barren Siberian wastes, he was startled by the huge body of greenish water and its "calm, dignified, dead beauty." He saw the ashen hills of Judea in the west, and watched the Moabite hills changing color until they burned red before sunset. He felt the torrid heat as he conducted his surveys with an eye toward building evaporation basins, studied the flow of fresh Jordan water in the Sea, examined the oil shale outcroppings as a possible fuel source, and then returned to Jerusalem with bottles of samples.

Early in 1920, Novemeysky re-established himself at the Dead Sea. He conducted experiments on the scene and began what turned out to be a seven-year fight to obtain from the British the right to exploit the Sea's minerals. During this long struggle, much of his laboratory work was done by scientists at the fledgling Hebrew University, high above the Dead Sea in Jerusalem. Immediately after the concession was granted, huge trucks began hauling building materials down the winding narrow road that sank from Jerusalem to the desert floor. Pumps and pipelines were installed to draw water to the evaporation pans and to bring sweet Jordan River water to wash the crystals in the carnallite sludge. By 1931, the plant produced its first large quantity of snow-white potash crystals. Three years later, a second plant was opened at Sdom. During World War II, the plants supplied the British, previously dependent on Germany for potash, with half of Britain's needs and more than 90 per cent of the potash required by British dominions other than Canada, which is a potash producer. By 1947, the two plants were selling over 100,000 tons of potash; today the figure is close to 1 million. During the War of Independence, the potash plants also provided base products needed in secret production of explosives first for the Haganah and then for the new Israel Defense Forces. In the 1948 war, the Arabs destroyed the plant at Kallia and besieged the one at Sdom. For some years after the end of the war, lack of adequate roads and transportation for its output kept the Sdom plant idle, but now it is the focus of a major industrial effort as Novemeysky's Siberian visions have become a subtropical success.

White-haired, lively-eyed, stocky Leo Picard is called Israel's pioneer geologist. Today, his spacious office is in the modern Hebrew University Groundwater Research Center in Ramat Gam. His career began in 1924, when, as a young German-born geologist, he sailed to Palestine as a fourth-class passenger. On board ship, he met Arthur Ruppin, then in charge of Zionist settlement activities. Asked what he intended to do in Palestine, Picard said, "Find water." Ruppin scoffed. Palestine has all the water it needs, he told Picard.

Thus began a long battle to prove that there was a major source of groundwater under Israel's hard limestone formations. Picard fought the Zionists, who wanted to drill only in the soft alluvial soils, and the British, who did not believe water could be found in the limestone mountains or at below-sea-level depths. Picard's simple view was that, if the Romans could do it, so could modern man, but few people would listen to a brash youngster holding a junior assistantship at the Hebrew University. Nevertheless, he worked hard at water exploration and at seeking other mineral resources.

Prior to World War I, water was pumped largely from shallow wells by small gasoline-engine-powered units. It was carried on animal back from communal wells. Jerusalem and other cities collected rain-water from rooftops and stored it in cisterns. Only a handful of communities had piped water; Petah Tikvah on the Yarkon had a diesel plant that pumped water to the orange groves. After the war, the first major attempt to improve the water supply was Rutenberg's hydroelectric development scheme. Some wells were improved, but the British obstructed water-seeking, using supposed lack of water as an excuse for forbidding or stalling Jewish settlement expansion. When Picard came to Palestine, only the German Army had done any major drilling and the Germans had not gone below 180 feet.

Roman success in finding water in the hardrock formations was still unknown. It was only much later that a Hadera farmer found, at Karkur, an ancient well that had been dug through limestone and dolomite. The primitive boring methods used in the early Jezreel Valley settlements could only dig shallow wells in softer strata. The use of explosives for well-digging began in 1929, but the antiquated machinery and nonprofessional supervision made this technique slow and expensive. Early attempts by French drillers to find water at 1,800 feet were unsuccessful and only served to confirm the prevailing view that there was no water in the bedrock.

There was, however, some progress in seeking and supplying

water in the 1930's. New drilling, pipe-laying, and storage techniques, aided by electricity from the new power plants, improved pumping- and irrigation-operations from the Jezreel Valley springs and the Jordan and Yarmuk rivers. A waterworks was built at Karkur, where the Romans had brought water up from beneath the rocks, and the Mekorot Water Company was founded in 1937 with six employees, among whom were Levi Eshkol, later to become Prime Minister of Israel, and Pinchas Sapir, now a Cabinet Minister. Mekorot's first project was piping well water from Haifa to nearby settlements near Nazareth and the Jezreel Valley. During its first year, the company supplied 18,000 cubic metres of water; thirty years later, it would supply over 722 million. World War II brought further development of water resources because of the need for food grown in Palestine, but rotary drilling on a large scale did not begin until 1946 or later, when oil-drilling companies loaned their equipment to Israeli engineers just before the War of Independence, which, unfortunately, interrupted all such operations. So important was water supply that engineers and pipelayers from Mekorot followed the embattled roadbuilders constructing the so-called Burma Road that lifted the siege of Jerusalem.

During the same period, agricultural settlement continued to expand. In the 1920's, the Jewish National Fund bought Jezreel Valley land, necessitating large-scale swamp-drainage projects. Settlement of the Zebulon Valley on the shores of Haifa Bay and into the central Sharon required more swamp-draining and special engineering to immobilize shifting coastal dunes. Farming on the eroded Judean Hills proved unsuccessful, so afforestation on the rocky hillsides was undertaken. In the late 1930's, spurred on by political developments, land settlement intensified, moving into the Beit Shean Valley, the upper western Galilee, the southern coastal plains, and the northern Negev. Problems were great, and varied. In the Beit Shean Valley, spring waters from Mount Gilboa had turned the gray-white marl soil into a brackish swamp, which had to be drained and desalinized. At Beit Ha'arava, sweet water from the Jordan was used to percolate out the salts. Areas marked by the British as unfit for cultivation became vineyards and orchards. In the south, settlements faced problems with the hard-covered loess soils, which were subject to gullying and erosion from desert winds, winter storm runoff, and flash floods. Nonetheless, water engineers brought in irrigation water, and, within only a year or two of their settlement, the first three Negev groups were farming successfully. Their unusual accomplishments—such as planting fruit trees at low points where water could be collected and contained by low earthen walls, or spreading out flash-flood waters—set the stage for today's large-scale desert agriculture.

Expanding along with agricultural settlement was the work of the Agricultural Research Institute. Aaron Aaronsohn's station at Athlit had closed down during World War I, but in 1920 the Zionist Organization authorized Wilkansky to establish a new center. His plans were aimed at three specific problems: the soil, climatic and related conditions, and the nature of the settlers themselves, with doubling the output per acre as the ultimate goal. Because the new farmers lacked agricultural tradition and experience, he predicted that their farms would be costly investments with poor output unless they had proper guidance. He called for a central institute, with a laboratory, library, and experimental fields, and for smaller stations scattered around the countryside, to provide on-the-spot research into specific soils and cultivation methods required for them.

The Institute so designed concentrated first on the heavy soils of the Jezreel Valley, where settlement development was slower than expected because of the lack of rain, the field pests, cattle disease, and shortages of funds. Intensive work by the Institute's field station helped solve the many problems. The Institute's work had great influence on Jewish farming. Experimental stations brought progress in cultivation, fertilization, and crop rotation. Prewar experimentation in cattle- and poultry-breeding was expanded along with important work on pest control and soil conditioning. The Jewish farmer's willingness to try anything paid off; while the British still downgraded agricultural developmental potential, Jewish farms were surpassing the minimum yields Wilkansky sought, and milk yields neared European standards.

Industrial development also increased. When Rutenberg began expanding his electrical service in 1924, there were sixty-one

Jewish factories and workshops in Tel Aviv. Two years later, the figure trebled, with building-materials manufacture ranking first, ahead of textiles, printing, and leather work. The industrial complex in Haifa now included a large flour mill and the Nesher cement factory. Sharply increased immigration from Germany in 1933 brought to Palestine many people with technical knowledge and experience in commerce and industry, which in turn abetted industrial growth. By 1937, there were 5,600 factories and workshops.

Another striking development during this same period was the Tower-and-Stockade concept of settlement in the Upper Galilee, where there had been no Jewish villages. Most of the land was surrounded by Arab holdings and far from main roads, so the villages had to be self-reliant. The Tower-and-Stockade method was the first introduction of prefabrication on a large scale. Ready-made sections of houses, watch-towers, and protective walls were carried to the scene and erected with help from other settlements. Within a day's time, bare ground would be covered by a solidly protected settlement, which had a bullet-proof double wall filled with earth and stones, a watchtower, a searchlight, and a generator for making electricity. Then the new villages were given essential farming equipment and guidance. Eventually, these fortified encampments became permanent towns with stone houses and large farm areas. By the time World War II began, they were an important source of food.

World War II isolated Britain from its European sources of supply and brought a tremendous industrial boom to Palestine, as well as an expanded need for food production. New industries sprang up in the bigger cities and in the villages and even in some of the *kibbutzim*. Agriculture expanded to meet the needs of the populace and the British troops in the Middle East. Still, there were shortages, and a determined effort was made to teach Arabs to eat Jewish food and vice-versa. By September, 1946, Jewish farmlands had grown to 450,000 acres.

The three leading academic wellsprings of Israeli science and engineering were also born during the post–World War I period.

The concept of a technical institute for the settlers evolved as early as 1907, and plans were made to open a technically oriented vocational high school in Haifa in 1912. But World War I intervened, and the Technion did not open its doors to students until February, 1925, emerging then as a full-fledged college rather than a high school. Four decades later, the first Technion Director, Arthur Blok, recalled:

> Palestine in 1924 was not Israel in 1965, and there were maddening shortages of the most obvious things. Not an electrical connector, a length of belting, and a hundred other things which had to be brought from Europe and then fought through customs. In all of Palestine, it appeared that there was only one reliable plumber, a German, and it was upon ingenuity in jumping the queue for his services that installation of the chemical laboratory depended. The fact that his original plumbing survives is testimony to his work. Another problem was the supply of water and electricity. Apart from rain-water tanks, the whole of Hadar Carmel depended for its water on the Technion well, which was leased to a company and was a source of much affliction. The pump was submerged about 100 metres down in the solid rock of the Carmel and driven by an oil engine and dynamo in the workshops. This highly temperamental plant divided its favors casually between lighting the Technion and pumping water, and its exhaust pop-popped nightly across the Carmel in competition with the howling of occasional jackals. To my dismay, I found one night that the whole steel framing of the workshop was electrically alive and might well have been so for years, although there was no record of anybody having been electrocuted.

The first Technion departments were architecture and civil engineering. There were twenty-six students, including one girl, in the first class. In his opening address, Blok asked, "Who knows what technical fruit may spring from the seed which is now being sown? . . . If in these days we lay the foundation of our work well and wisely . . . the house which we now start to build will in its completion be of transcendent effect in the greater task of building up again our land of Israel."

Since that day, Technion graduates have become the pioneering engineers who built roads and buildings, designed the irrigation system, drained the swamps and prepared a nation for incoming immigrants. Before the State of Israel was created, Technion was an important defense training center. Like the

Hebrew University and the Weizmann Institute, it played an important role in the War of Independence. David Ben-Gurion has called Technion "one of the cornerstones of the country's development."

The Hebrew University was formally dedicated the same year Technion enrolled its first students, although the idea of a Jewish University was first espoused, as early as 1762, by Jean-Jacques Rousseau. His vision was not put into practical terms until Dr. Hermann Schapira, a mathematics professor at Heidelberg University, presented a plan for a Jewish University in Palestine to the First Zionist Congress in 1897. The movement for the university was pushed by Herzl, Weizmann, Martin Buber, and Berthold Feiwel and by 1913 had gained enough momentum for the Eleventh Zionist Congress to authorize its establishment. The cornerstone was not laid on Mount Scopus until 1918 because of World War I. The ceremonies, held on the anniversary of the destruction of Jerusalem, first by the Babylonians and later by the Romans, took place while fighting between the Turks and the British was going on just twelve miles away.

Albert Einstein, Paul Ehrlich, and Weizmann participated in planning the University, which opened first as a research institute focusing on a revival of Judaism, the development of natural resources, and the creation of a medical program. The first occupied building was a research laboratory. Coincidentally, the last one completed before Arab military occupation closed down the Mount Scopus campus during the War of Independence was also for science.

Institutes for research in chemistry and microbiology were the first scientific units opened. And just as the first Technion director had problems with equipment, so did the first director of the microbiological institute. He was Saul Adler, a young British-trained physician with a distinguished record in tropical medicine and a Zionist desire to come to Palestine. He later recalled that, after writing to Weizmann for a faculty appointment, he was named an assistant in "the nonexistent microbiology institute of which I was the only member." Adler was given 200 pounds sterling for equipment, chemicals, and other materials. To these he had added his own microscope, dating back to his student days. There was no room for him on Mount Scopus, so he found space in the old Rothschild Hospital in Jerusalem where his "Institute" shared space with a hospital laundry passageway and the chief Hadassah bacteriologist, who worked with rabbits in the preparation of serum. All this in exchange for also serving as the Hadassah pathologist, which made him the only pathologist in the whole country. His budget for the Institute, including the salary of a laboratory technician, was 5 pounds a month.

On the occasion of his retirement in 1965, Adler recalled, "Everything then was on a minuscule scale; compared to a European University we were nothing, but we started the way most things were started in this country—with plenty of enthusiasm, no funds, and little staff. I still remember the tremendous emotion aroused by the opening of the University in 1925; the extent of the emotion bore no relation to the extreme poverty of the University."

Subsequently, the Institute became the Department of Parasitology and joined other departments as part of the medical center on Mount Scopus, and Adler's work with tropical diseases, water-borne diseases, leprosy, and sand-fly infections became world famous.

During the years before Israeli statehood, the growing University performed many important scientific services. Medical research helped raise the country's health standards, and, during World War II, courses were taught to Allied medical officers. University geologists and chemists assisted in searching for groundwater and for ways to exploit Palestine's limited natural resources. In the field of agriculture, the University did a great deal of research and established its own agricultural institute at Rehovot in 1940 to work closely with Wilkansky's station there and with the newly established Daniel Sieff Research Institute headed by Dr. Weizmann.

Ironically, during this pre-State era, the University's botanists were invited by the governments of Iraq and Syria to advise on forestry problems and on combating locusts. During World War II, University scientists did special research for the British armed forces; it was frequently referred to as "an arsenal of brains." In spite of this, during the last five months of the British Mandate,

Mount Scopus was cut off and the campus could be reached only by armored convoy. When the British left, the campus was shelled. The campus housed only a small military garrison until after the Six-Day War.

The Weizmann Institute, which today ranks as one of the world's great scientific research centers, began as the result of discussions in 1933 between Weizmann and Israel and Rebecca Sieff in London following the death of the Sieffs' son, a promising science student. Weizmann suggested a fitting memorial would be the establishment of a research institute in their son's name. He saw it as a place where prominent Jewish scientists driven out of Germany by Hitler could continue their work and serve the Jewish people of Palestine.

It was built on bare sand, at a site on Rehovot chosen by Weizmann because it was close to the ruins of Yavne, where the ancient Jews built a technical school in Roman days. He saw the Institute as a modern Yavne. He felt also that there should be one scientific institute near the coast because there was always a possibility that Jerusalem might be cut off some day, as, of course, it later was. Since it would also be close to the Agriculture Research Institute, Weizmann felt that the two units could make possible work of both current agricultural value and long-range basic research.

The Daniel Sieff Institute was opened on April 13, 1934. At the opening ceremonies, Weizmann said Palestine would be made to flourish by scientific research. (The inscription over the entrance says, "Work for this country. Work for science. Work for humanity.") One of the first scientists to join him was Dr. Ernst David Bergmann, a young organic chemist from Berlin who later became chairman of Israel's Atomic Energy Commission. Although the Institute was fairly close to the Mediterranean, where the climate is much hotter than in Jerusalem or Mount Carmel, the heat did not deter Weizmann from his own researches in industrial applications of microbiological chemistry. He also established a workshop so that the Institute could make its own equipment, and this shop has since become the large Instrument Engineering Center, with a research and development program of its own.

In 1944, on the occasion of Weizmann's seventieth birthday, the idea of renaming the Institute for him was proposed. Although Weizmann demurred, the Sieffs agreed. A year later, at a founder's dinner in New York, he said, "It is a tremendous satisfaction for a scientist to do pioneering work. The Jewish scientists will be in a position of intellectual pioneering for a great region which is today a bridge between three continents."

The establishment of the three great science and engineering centers, plus the back-breaking field work of men such as Rutenberg, Picard, Wilkansky, Wilbush, and Novemeysky and all of the workers who drained the swamps, built the drainage and water systems and electric power lines, and tilled the soil, had set the foundation stones for Israel's scientific and technological development. When, with the proclamation of the State and the War of Independence, a new nation came into being, the scientists of Israel were ready, imbued with purpose, schooled in ingenuity, tempered by climate and the fight to preserve their freedom, and convinced that the impossible could be done. Even the newest immigrant-scientist was further steeped in the almost instant tradition of what was to become the technology of necessity.

IV

Pulling It All Together

The State of Israel will be open to Jewish immigration and the ingathering of exiles. It will devote itself to developing the land for the good of all its inhabitants.—*from the Proclamation of Independence, May 14, 1948*

Technology is constantly proving that human resourcefulness can more and more overcome the limitations imposed by man by nature. . . . Certainly, no one is more entitled than we Israelis, with our poor endowment of natural resources, to make use of the achievements of science and technology . . . whatever is done or not done by our scientific institutions in large measure determines our fate and our ability to develop this small country and to defend it, while at the same time absorbing millions of immigrants from the Diaspora.—*from a speech by Prime Minister* LEVI ESHKOL *in 1965*

The early years of the new State were faced with many pressing problems, such as the absorption of large numbers of immigrants that had to be housed and employed at all cost . . . the great optimism and faith of that period that believed that anything was possible and an extraordinary ability to improvise in solving current problems [are] not conducive to quiet, long-term planning.— *from "Report on National Science Policy and Organization of Research in Israel," as revised in March, 1969*

43

On the telephone, Yeshuran Schiff was all but rude in response to a request for an appointment to discuss the building of the Eilat-Beersheba pipeline. Ex-cop, ex-schoolteacher, and one of Israel's top men in the field of pipeline construction, he crisply answered, "I have no time to talk about something that happened twelve or thirteen years ago. My mind is too busy with the future."

This attitude is not uncommon in Israel. Her scientists, engineers, and others who are concerned with harnessing technology for the future have too much to do in a country whose population has trebled since the nation came into existence twenty-two years ago. Israel is on a short-range collision course with its people's needs for not only food, housing, water, oil, and industrial growth, but also military survival. Nevertheless, its achievements and plans must be put into a historical context, which begins when the new State was proclaimed and opened the doors to the Jews of the world. At the end of 1948, there were 879,000 people in what had just become the Jewish nation. Of these, 101,828 arrived during the months *after* May 14, 1948. The next year, 239,576 came; the next, 170,249; and the next, 175,095. By the end of 1952, the population had almost doubled. Today, it is more than 2.8 million, well over three times what it was on that historic day as the leaders and citizens of the new government locked arms and sang the *Hatikvah* while Arab armies prepared to invade from all sides.

On that day, 412,000 acres were under cultivation, 75,000 of them irrigated, thanks to the extraordinary and heroic labors of the early settlers and the comparative handful of agronomists, botanists, water experts, and engineers who helped them find their way. Twenty years later, in 1968, the number of cultivated acres was well over 1 million, the number under irrigation was 410,000, and Israel was producing more than 80 per cent of the food it needed to feed a trebled population.

Those few figures are what the late Israeli Prime Minister Levi Eshkol—himself an early employee of the first water company—meant when he said, "Technology is constantly proving that human resourcefulness can more and more overcome the limitations imposed on man by nature," but they also reflect what a spokesman for the National Council for Research and Development was writing about when he said, in effect, "Okay, fellows, enough of this scientific *chutzpah;* we're an established nation now, so let's settle down and do things in an orderly way."

The rest of this book will recount the story of how Israel's technology of necessity met the test—and is still meeting it—in the face of massive immigration and the need to provide food, water, homes, jobs, defense, education, health, and a livable environment in a small land that is half desert and lacks, or is only partially supplied with, most of the basic resources other countries take for granted, and what's more, is surrounded by nations who have sworn to drive the new immigrants and their longer-established compatriots into the sea.

Before briefly reviewing the organization that has been achieved in the scientific and agricultural fields and that the National Council for Research and Development is seeking to advance even further, it might be well to tell the story of the man who wrote the 1969 report quoted at the beginning of this chapter. He should know about the problems of bringing long-range planning to the men who made reality out of one impossible dream after another.

He is London-born Harry Zvi Tabor, who earned his Ph.D. at the Hebrew University in 1959. Before coming to Israel, he did research for the British Boot Association and engineering and research for an electric meter company in London. In Israel, he became Principal Scientific Officer for Physics of the Israel Research Council formed by the new State. In 1951, he was named Director of the National Physical Laboratory of Israel, and has headed the government's Solar Energy Research Program since 1954.

Like so many Israeli scientists, Tabor is urbane, has many interests, and has left his mark—more than 100,000 marks, one might say—on the Israeli landscape. He is also a scientist who has seen his plans change direction with the result that, although he started out to do one thing, he wound up with not one, but two widely different, though related, achievements.

One resource Israel has in more than ample supply is sunlight. Tabor's goal was to harness the sun's rays as a source of energy during a period when the electric power supply was not keeping up with a growing population and what little oil had been discovered obviously was not enough for any extensive domestic uses.

His office is in a modern cement building on the lower level of the Hebrew University campus at Givat Ram. It looks out on a typically rocky hillside rising toward the Jewish National Museum. Inside the office, there is a prototype of the kind of solar battery being used to power space-age satellite communications equipment; outside the window, one can see the white fluted top of the beautiful Shrine of the Book, which houses the Dead Sea scrolls of an earlier Jewish civilization. One can also see an electric light pole carrying the power lines that finally superseded Tabor's researches into domestic uses of solar energy.

The first major use found for solar energy in Israel was for home hot-water heaters. They were powered by the sun's rays, absorbed on black painted metal surfaces connected to batteries that transformed the heat into electricity to warm the water. The first units were inefficient and costly because the black painted surface threw off too much heat after absorbing the sun's rays. By developing a new kind of treatment for the metal, Tabor and his associates were able to reduce the heat loss by 50 per cent and design an efficient, relatively low-cost home hot-water heating unit. During the next twelve or thirteen years, more than 100,000 of these heaters were installed. In many parts of Israel, every home and apartment-house roof top displays the flat, tilted solar energy collectors and the barrellike heating units to which they are connected.

As low-cost electricity finally spread throughout the country, the demand for the solar heaters has dwindled. However, Harry Tabor hasn't given up. He and the research team headed by Dr. Hannah Arbek have come up with a new cadmium sulphide cell (much less expensive than the costly silicon crystal cells used in outer space) and have two of their units in service, one powering a traffic signal at a nasty isolated curve and intersection on the Jerusalem–Tel Aviv highway and the other providing energy for a navigation buoy in the strategic Straits of Tiran. Unlike ordinary battery-powered units, they need servicing only once a year or even less frequently.

Seeking additional uses for his solar energy batteries, Tabor designed a low-pressure turbine that was two to three times as efficient as the usual small turbines. This, he felt, would be ideal for use in developing countries such as Israel because the unit is simple, self-contained, and requires little maintenance. However, his first customer, far from being an underdeveloped nation, was the American Telephone and Telegraph Company, which purchased the turbines to use at remote microwave relay stations. Now the turbines are being used in many places, but no one is hooking them up to solar energy sources. Undaunted, Tabor continues his research on more efficient, less expensive solar-energy batteries, happy that he has at least contributed a new turbine manufacturing industry to Israel and that, with or without solar energy, the turbines mean needed jobs for immigrants and export dollars for the nation's economy.

The moral of the story, if there can be said to be one, is that, although the long-range plans of Harry Zvi Tabor went aft aglee, they, nonetheless, met Israel's needs. Yet he is the man who decries the improvisational tradition as not conducive to sound planning.

Shortly before Tabor's solar-powered traffic light was installed during the summer of 1969, Israel had another striking example of how, when an expedient application is suddenly called for, technology can be used for something entirely different from what it started out to provide.

The Alliance Caeserea Polymer Industries Company manufactures polyurethane, the basic ingredient for foam-rubber mattresses and pillows. Polyurethane has excellent oil-absorbing properties. The company was experimenting with the use of polyurethane flakes in mat form to remove oil from the sea in harbor areas and had developed a new form of the polymer, which absorbed more oil and repelled more water. One great advantage to using polyurethane for this purpose is that it does not sink, as detergents do, and harm marine life.

The process was demonstrated for engineers from the Transport Ministry, Ports Authority, and Oil Pipeline Company in Haifa on May 18. Just thirteen days later, Alliance Caeserea

Manager Shlomo Dovrat received an urgent call from the Mekorot Water Company. Arab saboteurs had blown up the Tapline in the Golan Heights, and the escaping oil was flowing down the dry Banyias riverbed into the Jordan River and thence into the Kinneret (Lake Tiberias), endangering this important part of Israel's water supply.

"We threw an oil-absorbent boom across the Jordan River where it enters the Kinneret to catch any oil entering the Lake, and we attacked the oil patches in the northeastern section of the Kinneret with our floating carpets," Dovrat reported. "They gobbled up the oil like magic. No harm was done to the fish, which are abundant there, and the entire operation cost less than half what the Mekorot men thought it would cost."

Carl Keren, Director of the Center of Scientific and Technological Information, has an explanation for why this technology of improvisation and can-do seems so often to work almost magically. In his office on Hachashmonaim Street in a section of Tel Aviv that looks very much like the crowded industrial sections of midtown Manhattan or Jersey City—except that the streets are wider—he pores over reports and technical papers that reflect not only achievement but purpose and motivation. In his view:

> The paramount achievement of Israel and its technology is the integration of a population three times its original size. This includes helping large groups of people span centuries and technologies. Whether they want to or not, a great many people are still *getting involved* in what they are doing. People are living for something above and beyond their own personal lives. This is one of the things that makes things work . . . people want to help the state they live in. If you have a job to do, it is better to do it with a purpose. If you weighed everything from a cost-effectiveness point of view, you'd never do it.

Keren has been in Israel thirty-six years. He has seen the great changes in water supply, afforestation, crop selection, and education, all aimed at making possible physical and economic survival. "So much has changed in agriculture," he says. "It is so much greener . . . A poultry run today is really a factory for making eggs."

All of this happened after the State of Israel came into being. In existence at that time was a fairly good agricultural research infrastructure, built around the Agricultural Institute at Rehovot and the Hebrew University agricultural school there, and a well-developed system of extension services and on-the-spot research fields. The Daniel Sieff Institute, renamed for Chaim Weizmann, was providing additional agricultural research support. Three fish-research groups, dealing with fish culture, sea fish, and fish diseases, had been set up between 1942 and 1948. There had been some organized mineral and groundwater exploration, and the Hebrew University and the Technion were providing techno-logical and scientific resources in the realm of practical needs. Medical research was well advanced and had effectively wiped out tropical diseases in the country. The Mandatory Government had established a meteorological service, a forestry station, vet-erinary and hydrological institutes, and had encouraged the crea-tion of a Building Testing Station, which in 1945 became the Standards Institute of Israel. In 1942, the British had set up a Board of Scientific and Industrial Research to deal with war-effort-related problems and, after the war, had expanded it to include citrus-growing, quarrying, and building materials. Nove-meysky's Potash Company supported a research program carried out in cooperation with the Hebrew University's Department of Physical Chemistry.

As a result, the new government acquired a ready-made capa-bility in agriculture, medicine, the physical sciences, and engi-neering. But most of the institutions or research units were autonomous, financed from outside the country, and involved in the pre-State economic and political establishments.

The big question, then, was how to pull this all together to meet pressing needs and to focus on what had to be done. And, as in the pre-State days, there were—and still are—the problems of insufficient funds, urgent and immediate needs that took prece-dence over long-range planning, and intermittent major emer-gencies. When one takes an overview of the first twenty years of Israel's history as a nation, the major contributions of science and engineering can be seen in the tremendous growth of agriculture, the creation of a national water system, the spread of electricity, the growing development of the Negev, the creation of several major industries of vital importance to the nation—aviation, shipbuilding, petrochemicals, chemicals, and food processing, to name a few. And, at the same time that applied science and technology were meeting what might be called gut-level national needs, Israel's men of science and engineering were also gaining worldwide stature in the realm of pure, fundamental basic research. (In the 1970's, the Israeli Government would like more emphasis placed on applied research as compared to basic research, which might or might not some day have practical applications, and on industrial research, which has only in the past several years begun to grow appreciably.)

The first formally organized scientific research program under the new government was within the Israel Defense Force. This was, to some extent, a formalization of the clandestine activities carried on by the nation's scientists and engineers for the Haganah secret defense forces during the British Mandate days and was given immediate priority because Israel was born in the midst of a war with the Arab nations and had to fight for its existence for several months even as the new government took its first, formative steps.

The Research Council of Israel was established in January, 1949. Originally, under the chairmanship of Prime Minister Ben-Gurion, its members were twelve leading scientists. Subsequently, the leaders of the Hebrew University, the Technion, and the Weizmann Institute were added to the Council. The Council's purpose was to encourage scientific research aimed at enhancing the nation's economy. In 1949, it created a Geological Institute to study the country's mineral resources. This Institute drew heavily on the Department of Geology at the Hebrew University. That same year, a Dead Sea Research Laboratory was established to study the resources of the Dead Sea during a period of years in which the Dead Sea Works were inactive. The northern end of the Dead Sea was in Arab hands, and the works at the southern end could not be reopened until the completion of a spectacular roadbuilding project in 1953. In 1950, the National Physical Laboratory was created to standardize instruments, provide meteorology services, and carry out applied scientific research. In 1953, the Institute for Fibers and Forest Products was established to study textiles and the utilization of natural fibers. Two years later, the Negev Institute for Arid Zone Research was established in cooperation with UNESCO. The Council also tried to instigate industrial research associations such as those in Great Britain, where industry and the government share the costs, but what small industry existed at the time was not research oriented. Institutes were established, however, in the rubber, ceramics and glass, and paint fields. What little money the Council had to support research activities in the universities was not enough seriously to affect over-all science and research policy.

In addition to the Prime Minister's Office, there was considerable organized research activity in different ministries, particularly the Ministry of Agriculture, which took over the Jewish Agency's and Mandatory Government's research units and set up the Volcani Institute of Agricultural Research—still the largest applied research effort in the country—the Sea Fisheries Institute, and the Fish Pond Institute. The Ministry of Agriculture also administers the Hydrological Service under the direction of a water commissioner and works closely with Tahal, Water Planning for Israel, which was founded in 1952.

The Ministry of Development, which controls the large industries dealing with chemicals and minerals, established within these companies research laboratories dealing with mining, chemical fertilizers and phosphates, the Dead Sea Works, and related projects. The Ministry of Health has research laboratories in larger government hospitals and a special radio-isotope laboratory.

In 1959, the Research Council was succeeded by a larger National Council for Research and Development, which included representatives from the Treasury and ministries involved in research activities. This new Council has since added a number of research institutes dealing with such fields as pharmacology and fermentation and established, in cooperation with the United Nations, an Industrial Research Center at the Technion, a Bureau of Scientific Liaison, a Center for Scientific and Technological Information, and the Oceanographic and Limnological Agency. The Atomic Energy Commission was established as early as 1952, and its research activities include such practical, Israel-related areas as the physics and engineering of reactors, desalination by means of nuclear energy, and the use of isotopes. which, in Israel, were used to study the movement and structure of underground aquifers.

With support from the U.N. Technical Assistance Program, the government set up a Technical Advisory Board, comprised of international and local experts, to deal with over-all policies concerning exploitation of basic natural resources and the development of industries using those resources. This advisory body was terminated after eight years, in 1965, when it had achieved its objectives. In addition, the Knesset, Israel's Parliament, established the Academy of Sciences and Humanities in 1961 to advance scientific activity and to represent Israel in international scientific organizations.

In 1966–67, the last year for which figures were available, the Israeli investment in civilian scientific research and development (R&D) was about $37 million, about the same as for defense R&D. This amounts to about 2.2 per cent of the gross national product, approximately the same level as for Holland, France, Sweden, and Germany, but well below that of the United States. The number of research workers in the natural sciences and technology in Israel was about 2,900 that same year, or about 1 R&D scientist or engineer for every 1,000 people in the country. This is about the same proportion as in Great Britain or Japan, and it is higher than in Canada, Germany, France, Belgium, and the Netherlands.

More than 60 per cent of all the civilian research going on in Israel is in the universities, including the Weizmann Institute, which is a post-graduate institution. The government institutes carry out about 25 per cent of the total research effort; industrial research accounts for 12 per cent, and the remainder is largely medical research conducted in hospitals and elsewhere. Although government-funded and industrial research is almost entirely applied studies, the major share of the research at the institutions of higher learning is basic, and is funded from the institutions' regular budgets and from special grants from either Israeli sources or foreign foundations and contracting agencies. Many of the latter have been U.S. Government agencies or agencies of the

United Nations. Because this research is funded independently of the Israeli Government, problems of coordination and allocation of facilities have arisen. However, government support of university budgets has passed the 60 per cent mark (at the Technion, it is over 70 per cent), and these problems may become less and less important.

Even though government studies tend to decry, or at least to appear concerned about, the high level of basic research in the universities, there is ample evidence that, when there is a need, the university scientists and engineers come through. This is especially true in the defense areas, but equally true elsewhere. Even the esoteric science of the Weizmann Institute has provided important assistance to the search for oil, study of earthquake problems, and use of isotopes in underground water surveys, as well as in the agricultural field. The Technion has been an engineering mainstay of national development; it is not uncommon for Technion researchers to cross fields in unexpected ways. The Aeronautical Engineering faculty, for example, has undertaken extensive research into the development of industrial furnaces to be constructed in Israel rather than imported at high cost and then, as a spin-off from that research, utilized the same laboratory equipment that was being used to study fuel injection sprays to help the citrus-growers with problems related to insecticide spraying methods. Also out of the aeronautical research laboratories has come a promising new heat exchange process for desalination. Hebrew University researchers have made many important practical contributions to agriculture, mining, water supply, and irrigation concepts and worked closely with the Meteorological Service in studying and implementing the world's only organized cloud-seeding program, which is now a regular part of the Israeli water supply program.

It is interesting, too, to note that all three of these institutions have helped organize the new University of the Negev and provided faculty for its initial courses. The Technion and the Hebrew University have also been closely allied with the new University at Haifa.

Nuclear research is conducted at the Weizmann Institute, the Hebrew University physics labs, the Technion, which deals in nuclear engineering, and the University of Tel Aviv, which also does some specialization in research related to space problems. There are two nuclear reactor centers, the Nahal Sorek Nuclear Research Center, which has a reactor of the "swimming pool" type using enriched uranium for fuel, and the larger Negev Center at Dimona using natural uranium. The focal points of Israeli nuclear research are nuclear physics and chemistry, reactor physics and engineering, desalination, application of isotopes and high-powered radio sources, metallurgy and electronics, radiobiology and nuclear medicine. As to whether or not Israel has developed nuclear weapons, one doesn't ask and one isn't told. For many years, the very existence of the reactor at Dimona was kept a secret; its silvery dome-shaped building was variously described to curious tourists as a cement plant or an Arab mosque!

It takes 233 pages in *Scientific Research in Israel* (Tel Aviv: Center for Scientific and Technical Information, 1969) to describe all of the various research institutions that existed in the country in 1969; there is not a vestige of existing or potential national need that is not covered by one or more of them, and strong efforts are being made to tighten the coordination of effort. Scientific research today is expensive, and every piece of expensive equipment—computers, accelerators, electron microscopes, for example—must be used to the fullest. At the Weizmann Institute, engineers build their own computers to save money and to tailor them to specific needs, yet, when the Israeli shipyards built computerized warships, foreign-made computers were purchased and installed in the interest of time. Although Israel may be interested in developing a computer software industry, it is believed unrealistic to go into commercial production of computer hardware in view of the highly competitive world market that already exists.

There is currently a growing emphasis on industrial research to create science-based industries that will bring in export income. In this connection, the three major universities have all established research and development corporations that undertake the necessary research and are encouraging the development of what might be called science-based industrial parks close to the universities so that the university science and engineering facilities can be used on a close working basis by the industries. The Weizmann Institute, for example, is closely allied with companies making biomedical equipment and biological and plastic products; the Technion is allied to electronics and other firms.

One great advantage deriving from Israel's small size and deep sense of national purpose is the ability to mobilize technology and manpower in a time of crisis. The building of the Eilat-Beersheba pipeline is a case in point. It is also another illustration of the way in which Israeli technology is inextricably linked with national survival.

"Israel is taking a giant step along the road to economic independence with a pygmy-sized 8-inch diameter steel pipeline." So began a news story in the *Jerusalem Post* on February 26, 1957. Dramatic as that sounds, it was an understatement.

Immediately following the Sinai campaign in late October, 1956, Israel faced an oil crisis. Prior to that first successful effort to clear the Sinai of threatening Arab military forces, Israel got most of her oil from Soviet Russia and Venezuela. Crude oil was purchased for domestic consumption, bunker oil to fuel the electric power plants. After the brief fighting was over, Russia joined the United States in condemning Israel (the only time both the United States and Russia sided together against Israel) and the Soviet Union canceled its signed oil contracts with the Israelis. The Israelis had to find another source of oil. In the aftermath of the Suez campaign, the price of shipping oil from the United States or South America to the port of Haifa became prohibitive.

Fortunately, a new moderate regime had taken over in Iran and soon found it had a lot of oil to sell but no one to sell it to. Israel bid on the oil and bought it, for delivery to the Red Sea port of Eilat. The distance between the Persian Gulf and Israel was a lot shorter than from any other source of oil available to Haifa. Eilat was also potentially a seaport gateway for shipping from Israel to Asia and Africa. The urgencies of the situation fortuitously provided the opportunity to put Eilat on the map by developing the port facilities, even though, at the time, Israel didn't have much to export to African or Asian markets.

To utilize Eilat as an oil port, however, it had to be made into one, and means had to be found to move the oil from the port to the refineries in Haifa. There was no good road to Eilat; the nearest railhead was at Beersheba, 147 miles away. Between the two towns lay the Negev and its torturous deserts and bleak mountains and craters. What's more, time was the most important factor, for Israel was literally running out of oil.

Tahal, although a water planning company, was asked to draw up a plan for a pipeline; Mekorot, the water supply company, was assigned responsibility for building it. There were no topographical maps, terrain studies, or geological surveys of the area, and there was no time to make them. Also, there was no pipe, and no time to import it.

In charge of the operation were two Israeli engineers, Yeshuran Schiff, the tall, white-haired Palestine-born former school teacher and head of the Israeli CID, and Israel Libertovsky, who had come to Palestine in 1925 and was a graduate of the Technion. Short, cocky, a veteran of the Palmach striking forces of Haganah and the British army, and once second-in-command of illegal immigration to Israel, Libertovsky was working as an engineer for Mekorot. He was familiar with the Negev, having served there as military commander for the Israel Defense Forces. He already had behind him a distinguished record in water engineering, having built the country's only underground pumping station and directed the laying of a water pipeline through the Galilee in which the water climbed a 60-degree slope under a pressure of 90 atmospheres, the first such engineering feat in Israel.

Sitting in his noisy office in the Israeli shipyards thirteen years later, Libertovsky's pale blue eyes twinkled as he remembered the few ground rules laid down by the government: "Get it working. Make it quick. Whatever you need, you'll get. No red tape. No approvals needed."

The first step was to get two engineers to work out the plans, which were, simply, build it in six parts—four stretches of pipeline worked on simultaneously, two terminals to be built at either end, with proper offshore and train-yard oil transfer connections. In one week, the plan was ready. It was approved on November 28, 1957, by the government. A week later, survey teams had planted stakes and flags along the entire route. Earth-moving equipment and trucks converged on the area, the equipment coming from all over the country. (One chemical company at Oron later reported it could not meet its export quotas because twelve of its twenty trucks were working for the pipeline in the Negev.)

At the same time, the Tsinorot Joint Steel Pipe Company in Ramle, between Tel Aviv and Jerusalem, converted its equipment and began turning out nearly 450 sections of the wrapped eight-inch steel pipe every twenty-four hours. Each section was about thirty-five feet long. The pipe was loaded on freight trains, moved daily to the Beersheba yards, offloaded onto heavy-duty trucks and taken over jerry-built dirt roads to whatever point the snake-like channel had reached that day. Coordination between field headquarters and each section of the pipeline operation was carried out by shortwave radio and by Libertovsky using a Piper Cub airplane that had been assigned to him.

The pipe, coated with asphalt and wrapped in asbestos felt to ward off underground corrosion, was welded together and moved into the ditches, whose depths were determined by such requirements as: security against Arab marauders, reinforcement of the steel tubing with earth banked around it, and insulation of the oil against lower temperatures that might congeal the paraffin in the crude oil and block the pipes. Three pumping stations were installed, using machinery left behind by the British, who had disposed of it after plans to irrigate large areas of groundnut farms had failed. Designed for water, the pumps were put to work in an Israeli oil line.

Meanwhile, in Eilat, there were other difficulties. The tiny sea-coast village had no local craftsmen who could do the work of building an oil port. Crews had to be brought in, and a berth for the first tankers had to be formed with barges. Naval vessels were used to lower pipes into the water, and fishing boats were pressed into service to tow equipment and supplies. "When you need things, you do what you have to," Schiff says. "A proper engineer would have condemned the whole project."

The deadline for the project was approximately 100 days. This was so unbelievable that, when Prime Minister Ben-Gurion

visited the operations just after they started and asked Liber-
tosvky when the pipeline would be completed, his reply to
Libertovsky's prediction of three and a half months was, "In
which year?"

Surveys had to be made while the work progressed. The labor
—the project provided jobs for 800 Jewish and Arab laborers—
was inexperienced: In some places, men with pneumatic drills
had to drive the channels through solid rock. Yet every joint was
tested, every valve and seam in the storage tanks inspected. One
Canadian oil-installation superintendent working for one of the
contractors said that in twenty years' experience he had never
seen a job of this size and design completed so quickly.

The night before the first American tanker arrived from
Djibouti, Eliat was the scene of frantic activity. The last plates
were still being welded onto the top of the offloading tanks. One
old welder worked through the night and couldn't unbend his
fingers at daybreak. He had to be carried down. Every foreman
on the job lost his voice from shouting orders.

At 3:10 P.M. on April 7, 100 days from the start of operations,
the first tanker eased through a sandstorm that blocked the view
of the nearby Jordanian shore, flying an Israeli flag along with
the Stars and Stripes. That night there was a wild reception for
the ship's crew, with bearded waiters and sun-blackened workmen crowding the Tnuva Restaurant. Even then, the work was
not finished, for completion at the Beersheba end of the line was
still in process when the tanker started pumping oil into the
Eliat storage tanks at dawn the following day. As the first oil
began to flow toward Beersheba, men with Geiger counters
followed its progress, checking the whereabouts of isotopes
placed in the oil for signs of leaks.

Before the job was finished, plans were already under way to
build a 16-inch pipeline to replace the one just built. The original
pipe, which carried 1 million tons of oil its first year, is now being
used to transport water in the Negev, and a massive 42-inch line
now snakes its way through the Negev toward the new Mediterranean port of Ashdod and the Ashkelon oil fields. There are
roads now, and the big trucks hurtle around hairpin turns with
their heavy loads, but even the sight of the great new engineer-

ing achievements cannot dim the luster of the 8-inch pipeline that preceded them.

To meet this oil crisis, technology, machines, and manpower were almost miraculously mobilized. On the other side of the coin, however, the scientists and engineers seeking solutions to important but less pressing problems must often stretch their equipment as far as it will go, and then some, for it is hard to come by. At the end of 1968, there were only fifteen electron microscopes in Israel, or on order. Only one, at the Technion, was available for industrial research, and that one was being turned into a veritable workhorse for basic research, teaching, *and* industrial research. It was serving the departments of Metallurgy, Electrical Engineering, Physics, Chemistry, Sanitary Engineering, and Mineral Engineering. One of its uses, interestingly, was to catalog solid pollutants in the air around Haifa.

Considering the fact that Libertovsky had to take trucks away from other industries to build his pipeline, and that one of the most famous Israeli weapons of the War of Independence was fashioned from steel axles taken from railroad locomotives, one somehow suspects that the Technion people will make do until such time as the coordination the National Council for Research and Development is seeking to optimize takes effect.

In the meantime, the miracles still occur, and the impossible gets done. Where else would mattress stuffing defeat an oil slick?

V

You Can Get Water out of a Stone

Many years ago, Theodore Herzl wrote in *Altneuland*, a fictional account of the future Jewish nation in Palestine:

"The true founders of 'Altneuland' were the water engineers . . . everything depended upon them."

Probably no more truly prophetic statement has ever been made about Israel, for its very existence depends on having enough water for people, for irrigation, for industry. Because of this absolute necessity, the technology of water supply has been raised to a higher and more comprehensive level in this one small country than anywhere else in the world. No other country in the world knows as much about how much water it has, and where that water is. Nor has any other country done so much to harvest every possible drop through an integrated water supply system that encompasses a handful of undependable rivers, one medium-sized lake, highly variable rainfall, underground rock-bound aquifers, wells, cloud-seeding, and reclaimed sewage, and manages also to capture the occasional flash floods that course across the hard-crusted surface of the desert. Israeli water technology ranges from desalination to a new water-saving design for flush toilets. And working hand in glove with the water engineers are other scientists trying new ways of making the most of each hard-won gallon in a ceaseless effort to keep pace with the growing water needs of a growing nation.

Israel's "water engineers" are a colorful and widely varied crew, and they work in just as wide a variety of fields. On a given summer day, one might find graying Leo Picard kibitzing, while a drill crew bores down through limestone formations looking for water; Jacob Bear running figures through a Technion analogue computer to predict the future status of underground water storage in light of the year's rainfall patterns; and Chaim Cohen, of the Negev Institute for Arid Zone Research, on top of an experimental reverse-osmosis desalination unit at Yotvota, watching a young technician sweat in the 105°F. temperature while he tries to find a sponge rubber ball which had got stuck in one of the dozens of slender tubes that form the guts of the unit. Meanwhile, Zadek Ramm is supervising the interconnection of a captured Egyptian desalting plant to Israel's first multistage flash unit in a cul-de-sac cut into a hillside at Eilat, and, far to the north, in Haifa, Technion's Abraham Kogan runs metal pellets through a new desalting heat-transfer process. And, at the same time, the Hebrew University's Dan Goldberg will be busily checking crop yields at a desert experimental farm, using his fabulously successful trickle irrigation method, which uses a minimum of water for a maximum result. Not too many miles away, other Hebrew University researchers are checking the fruit on trees growing in the middle of the Negev, where there hadn't been any rain in six months and no modern irrigation at all was taking place.

They are all "water engineers" in the sense that Herzl used the words, and they are all part of the technological battle to stave off future water shortages that today seem all but inevitable. Theirs is a battle to accomplish the impossible. As of right now, they *are* doing the impossible. Presumably, they will go right on doing it.

In the tiny, unimpressive offices of the Israeli Hydrological Services, hard by a tire factory and soup company plant in

Jerusalem's small industrial section, Menachim Cantor, Commissioner of Water in the Ministry of Agriculture, quietly summarizes what has been accomplished since the State of Israel became responsible for the country's water supply. His simplicity belies the tremendous scientific and engineering achievements involved.

One accomplishment he describes as "unusual" is the operation of underground aquifers as annual and perennial reserves that are recharged regularly with waters from the Jordan project, captured floods and flash floods, municipal wastes and, of course, some of whatever rainfall there is in a given year.

Another "unusual" achievement is interrupting the normal hydrological cycle to capture water draining into the Mediterranean from the coastal aquifers and pumping it back into that vast underground storage area.

Also, he adds, "not many countries" have their entire water system in closed pipes and lined canals, which eliminate significant losses. Instead of "not many," he might have said, "no other countries."

And, as a fourth suggestion of the "unusual," he notes that Israel is the only country that does not use flood irrigation with the water running through open ditches to exposed furrows, but uses instead highly controlled sprinkling and newly developed underground trickle systems operated automatically by sensors imbedded in the soil. Near Eilat, he mentions casually, this new system has turned part of the Arava desert into one of the most profitable agricultural areas in the country, adding equally as casually that the desalination plant at Eilat runs at 105 per cent of rated capacity. All of this in a piece of geography that would seem to be in an extremely unfavorable position insofar as water is concerned.

Israel's semiarid climate is characterized by rainfall limited to four or five winter months with average annual amounts ranging from twenty-eight inches in the north to less than two inches in the south, at Eilat. Over 75 per cent of all the water resources are north of Tel Aviv, whereas most of the land suited to irrigation is in the south. Because of the limited water supply, less than half the arable land in the country is under cultivation.

What's more, only some of the rain that reaches the ground

stays there. As much as 60 per cent returns to the atmosphere from the soil or plants, 35 per cent is soaked up by the soil, and 5 per cent runs down winter streams or flooded wadis to the Mediterranean or the Jordan. In addition, the equivalent of 20 per cent of the total annual water supply is lost to evaporation from the surface of the Kinneret, the country's one large fresh-water lake, which lies baking in the hot sunshine 700 feet below sea level.

Prior to the establishment of the State of Israel, water supply depended mainly on surface waters, wells, and cisterns. Groundwater exploration was confined largely to the coastal plains where one didn't have to go down too far to find it. Sporadic investigations by Picard and others around Mount Carmel and in the Galilee, sponsored by the Jewish Agency and the Jewish National Fund, began in 1943. Sweet-water wells were established in the Negev by Mekorot to supply the Beersheba-Gaza plain. During the latter part of World War II, additional resources were found in the Galilee and around Carmel, groundwater was found in the foothills of the Ephraim Mountains, and a beginning was made at finding water in the Nubian sandstone beneath the Arava, the large desert valley that runs through much of the southern Negev. In 1952, a rich water strike was made more than 1200 feet down in the rock near Beersheba, and during this same period large supplies were found to furnish the Western Galilee. Deep drilling, at Picard's insistence, found other rich wells in the area from Lod to Wadi Ara.

The history of water planning in Palestine has had its ups and downs. When the League of Nations established the British Mandate and drew the boundary lines, all of the Jordan River and Lake Tiberias were placed in Palestine because they represented the only major water supply for the territory. Subsequently, American engineer James Hays's 1947 plan for a TVA on the Jordan and Eric Johnston's more recent one for joint Israeli-Arab use of the Jordan watershed foundered on Arab refusal to participate, although Israel has never taken more water from the Jordan than was envisioned in the Johnston plan.

The Jordan, in any case, is an undependable source of supply because of tremendous variations in its annual rate of flow, which depends to a large extent on the rainfall over its watershed area and the recharge of the underground springs that feed it and the Kinneret.

Because of fluctuations in the amount of surface water available from year to year and the unfavorable rainfall patterns, Israel has had to devise an extremely flexible national water system utilizing all possible water sources and means of transporting and storing the water. The system works; it makes possible the most efficient use of available water by overcoming the basic maldistribution as well as the seasonal and annual variations in water harvests.

Israel's first long-term economic plan was in the field of water supply. It was adopted in 1950 and included a preliminary inventory of the land and water resources, a list of high-priority projects and programs for further studies and pilot projects. By 1961, the plan had been enlarged to include a detailed water inventory, demand forecasts, and basic data for proposed projects. These plans serve as the frame of reference for Israel's water laws, which make all water from any source public property. Its development and use must be licensed and is regulated by the government.

With the adoption of the first plan, the race against time and need began. It has never really stopped, for, between 1948 and 1966, the use of proven water resources rose from 17 per cent to almost 90 per cent, including use of water from the Jordan and the Yarkon (the coastal groundwater aquifer), the Kinneret, and smaller resources. During the same period, the acreage under irrigation grew from 70,000 to over 400,000 and agricultural production increased sevenfold in spite of the fact that one half of Israel's farmers had gone to the land for the first time during the past fifteen years. This high rate of productivity and a very high use of water project capacity were made possible because of close coordination between the water planners at Tahal and the Ministry of Agriculture and the engineers at Mckorot.

Out of all this effort came an integrated water system that interconnects all major water sources and storage facilities while meeting all of Israel's major water needs, with the exception of those of the desert areas in the far south that are served by regional projects.

This was accomplished by a series of research and engineering projects unique in water supply history, which followed what Aharon Wiener, Director-General of Tahal, calls the ten commandments of water policy:

(1) Increased yields by adequate manipulation of the natural hydrological cycle.

(2) Improvement of the mineral and biological quality of substandard waters.

(3) Enhanced dependability of supply.

(4) Provision of water by 'squeezing,' i.e., by reducing the demand.

(5) Provision of water by changing the resources base.

(6) Provision of water by exploiting the engineering system up to its economic limits.

(7) Increased yields of water through integrating the supply system.

(8) Inducing changes in natural conditions which affect the hydrological cycle, with a view to increasing water yields.

(9) Increased supplies in the system through selective utilization of substandard waters.

(10) Provision of fresh water through desalting of saline groundwater and of seawater.

The keys to what has happened in Israel up to now are found in how some of these commandments were followed, and the future will depend upon others. It would be well to keep them in mind as a frame of reference.

At present, the major Israeli water sources directly or indirectly connected to the national water grid are the Upper Jordan and its tributaries, including the Kinneret and the Beit Shean spring area, which provide 37 per cent of the total average annual water yield of about 1,450 million cubic meters; the groundwater formations of the mountains in the Galilee and the Valley of Esdraelon, which are a part of the regional Kishon-Esdraelon system and also include spring flows, storm runoff, and reclaimed Greater Haifa area waste water (9 per cent); the groundwater system in the two coastal aquifers, which also are recharged by waste waters from many coastal communities (29.5 per cent); the Yarmuk River, which is also part of the Yarmuk project system stretching from Tel Aviv to the Negev (14 per cent); storm runoff from the major coastal intermittent streams, which is captured and stored in one of the coastal aquifers (5.5 per cent); and some reclaimed waste water from the Tel Aviv metropolitan area, which is also stored underground and fed into the water system moving south to the Negev.

Before this system was developed, more than half of Israel's water supply came from surface waters, which were undependable and frequently of poor quality. During the 1970's, three-quarters of the supply will be groundwater. Seemingly the ultimate proof of Leo Picard's geological pudding, this utilization of the underground aquifers involves a great deal more than just finding the water.

According to Wiener, "Most water planners in developing countries consider the emphasis given to groundwater development and underground storage . . . to be a racket invented by hydrological eggheads in order to bring confusion to the straightforward engineering programs of the hydraulic and civil engineering professions." He attributes this opposition to the difference between the problem-solving processes involved. Surface water is visible, you can measure its flow, and you deal with it by building traditional dams and other engineering structures. Groundwater, on the other hand, is invisible, can be evaluated only indirectly, and problem-solving depends on resources manipulation and management rather than simple engineering. The use of groundwater, he says, requires the "substitution of brain for brawn."

For Israel, it took a combination of brain and brawn to tie the whole water supply package together. Groundwater, including water from springs, represents about 80 per cent of the country's currently available water supply. In spite of the need for pumping it from deep wells in some areas, it is the most accessible water source and the best distributed in terms of the areas in which it is needed. The further development of other water resources—such as the Jordan River, collecting storm runoff, and reclaimed sewage—is costlier and more complex, although this, too, will have to be accomplished. An extremely important advantage for Israel is that utilization of groundwater does not call for construction of dams and creation of surface storage reservoirs. Topographically and geologically, Israel is generally unsuited for such construction except in a few places. In addition, the use of underground storage diminishes the danger of contamination and also, importantly for a hot Middle Eastern climate, virtually eliminates the loss of water through evaporation.

To utilize fully the aquifers—which are, in effect, large underground reservoirs created by the settling of different rock layers or faults developed from earth shifting—first the water planners had to know their extent, their depth, and how the water moved through them. Even though underground water moves in these vast subterranean reservoirs, it can take months or years for it to move from the point of intake to the sea or to a spring from which it bursts forth to start the whole hydrologic process over again.

In the mid-1950's, Israel's water planners made several efforts to determine the extent and movement of these underground resources. First, they tried to use dyes or chemicals to "label" the water so they could track its progress from test well to test well or from test well to spring. But the ground absorbed the dyes, and chemicals were hard to distinguish from other natural constituents of the soil through which the water passed as it seeped through the layers of sand and rock toward the aquifer. In 1957, the Weizmann Institute's Department of Isotope Research recommended to Tahal that radioactive isotopes be used. With funds from the Ford Foundation and later from other sources, the Weizmann scientists developed isotopes using radioactive iodine, cobalt, and irridium, which were cheap, longlasting, safe, and resistant to soil absorption. They were negatively charged so they would not be absorbed by the negatively charged ions in Israeli soil. The Institute designed the apparatus to check the radioactivity of the test wells.

A typical aquifer mapping problem in which the isotopes were used involved the waters of the Yarmuk River, which flows for twelve miles near Tel Aviv. During the rainy winter, the surplus water used to flow to the sea. Now, the Israeli engineers were pumping the surplus into wells in the natural rock formations so that it could be stored and used in the summer when the Yarmuk's flow was low and sluggish. But they had to make certain the storage aquifer was not the one that supplied the springs which fed the Yarmuk; if they used the same storage area they would just be pumping the water back into the river and thence back onto its path to the Mediterranean. The springs were monitored for however long it took the water to seep through—usually months.

In other experiments, the water engineers were able to tell the size of the water-holding rock strata by forcing isotopes into wells, then sucking them out again, and submitting the changes in the isotope to mathematical analysis.

Although the Weizmann Institute has long since finished this particular project, its scientists are still doing extensive work in the chemistry of water. They have also determined the amount of water lost from the Jordan by evaporation and how much flows into it from springs and smaller tributaries.

One story that has become legend in Israeli water circles, and which Jacob Bear at the Technion says is true, concerns a dam built at Ein Kerem, stopping up a large wadi through which winter rains flow. Ein Kerem is in the Judean hills outside of Jerusalem (the Hadassah Hospital complex high on a mountaintop there looks down on the Ein Kerem dam, standing most of the time on guard over a *dry* ravine). Shortly after it was built, winter storms filled the small reservoir behind the dam, but soon all of the water disappeared, and not into the valley. An intensive search for the missing water brought to light an extensive aquifer system, which is now being regularly put to use for water storage.

The kind of hydrological-cycle manipulation represented by the pumping of excess wint_r flow from the Yarmuk River for use during the dry summer months, when the river drops and flows sluggishly along, is a basic pattern for the whole integrated Israeli water system. On a larger scale, when the Kinneret threatens to overflow because of heavy winter rains, the water is now pumped through the National Water Carrier to large storage aquifers along the coast and held there for use during the dry season, or even later. Israel is no longer subject to drought-caused water shortages because it is able to save up the winter excesses against an unrainy day—or year—utilizing available surface water in the National Water Carrier during periods of high availability, while at the same time recharging the aquifers against the dry spells. Ultimately, one-half of all the available surface water from the rivers, storm runoff, and reclaimed sewage will be turned into groundwater.

One major problem that this water-engineering ingenuity is solving is the situation created by years of overpumping the coastal aquifers, first to be tapped by the growing nation. As the water level dropped, there was increasing encroachment by the sea as well as increasing salination because of the decreased flow of the water seaward. To correct this situation, water is not only pumped into the aquifer from the National Water Carrier, but wells have been sunk to intercept the water moving to the Mediterranean. It is then piped back to other wells or sandy areas where it falls back into the aquifer.

Tied into this approach is the Dan Region Water Reclamation Project, a Tahal effort to reclaim the waste waters of the Tel Aviv metropolitan area, in which about a million people live. This is believed to be the largest project of its kind anywhere in the world. The waste waters, from the sewage system—which carries domestic and industrial wastes—normally flow into the sea, and have, incidentally, created a considerable pollution problem for the beach-going Tel Avivians.

Use of reclaimed waste water is not unusual, and it is done in several places in Israel as well as in other countries, but never has it been attempted on so large a scale. Frequently, such water is used for irrigation purposes during the dry seasons, and some few smaller communities do store their waste water when it is not needed for irrigation. But without available surface reservoirs or a tremendous manufactured storage tank capacity, this could never be done for the amount of water being disposed of by an area the size of Tel Aviv and its environs, and there is not enough industry in or near Tel Aviv to utilize that amount of water for cleaning, cooling, and transporting materials. So the answer with which Tahal came up was groundwater recharge.

The aquifer is there, and so are large tracts of sand dunes to the south, which are not likely to be developed for residential or agricultural purposes. Beginning in 1960, the feasibility of the project was studied. Test ponds were created to see if the natural soil layers below the dunes would permit the water to pass through without clogging by solids or chemicals remaining in the effluent after it had undergone bacterial purification. Some 300 observation wells were sunk for geological mapping of the area, and it was found that, by letting the water seep through for three days, then leaving the test ponds dry for a week, a steady and desirable rate of percolation could be maintained. The first test ponds were built near Ashkelon, thirty-one miles south of Tel Aviv, using effluent discharges from Ashkelon itself. Additional tests showed that, as the water moved underground and was diluted by the cleaner water in the aquifer, the proportion of undissolved salts and other solids was so reduced that the water was potable according to the high standards of the U.S. Public Health Service, with the possible exception of occasionally higher than recommended concentrations of nitrates.

From the experiments, it was concluded that the project is feasible geologically, hydrologically, and in terms of town planning. With the exception of the nitrates, the water would be potable and would meet all of the agricultural requirements except for an excessive chloride content (water from the Dan region has a high chloride content to begin with). It would have to be mixed with at least twice as much water from other sources because it was going to be piped to southern Israel, and new industries in the area would have to be planned carefully to exclude those that would add harmful wastes to the effluent. In both this and a similar study conducted by Technion people for Tahal in the Haifa area, it was recommended that industrial communities should have two sewer systems, the second to carry off undesirable salts and chemicals while the first took water to the reclamation projects. If finances permit planned construction, this single Dan River region reclamation project will return hundreds of millions of usable gallons of water daily to the National Water Carrier, which will transport it to the arid Negev desert communities. It is hoped that the project will be completed by 1980.

Israel's groundwater projects have also served the purpose of upgrading the quality of the surface water and making it more available. The natural flow rate, formerly subject to seasonal and cyclical fluctuations, has been transformed into an underground supply usable according to demand rather than availability. Springs have been manipulated by interception or recharging the water into the aquifer, for withdrawal at a pumping station nearer the point of use. The mineral quality of the supply in some instances is improved by intercepting the underground flow feeding springs and pumping it around areas where it would pass through undesirable mineral deposits; the biological quality of the recharged water is improved because of the purifying action of its flow through the underground formations.

The National Water Carrier itself and the grid to which it connects are both impressive. Construction was a triumph of Mekorot engineering, for the Carrier takes water from the Kinneret and raises it hundreds of feet to a level whence it can flow downhill to the south. Its total length is somewhat over eighty miles, and it took four years to build, employing an average of 2,500 workers a day.

The idea of using the Kinneret as a national reservoir on which such a system could be based was put forward by W. C. Lowdermilk, the American agricultural engineer who is closely linked to early developments in Israel and who organized the Technion's Department of Agricultural Engineering. The Kinneret covers an area of about 100 square miles and holds almost 4 billion cubic meters of water, or well over a trillion gallons. It is replenished annually by water from the Dan, the Senir, and the Hermon, as well as from smaller streams and springs. Occasionally it is overfilled, as indicated earlier, but its linkage to the underground aquifers many miles away no longer makes this a wasteful occurrence.

The first step of the system comprises steel-jacketed reinforced pipes, which were towed into place by trawlers and installed by divers in a trench at the bottom of the lake. These pipes lead the Kinneret water into the Eshed-Kinrot pumping station in a cavern hollowed out of solid rock to protect it from Arab artillery and bombing attacks. The pumps raise the water from a point more than 640 feet below sea level to the system's first canal, which is over 130 feet above sea level. It is no wonder that Israel Libertovsky, the project engineer, later was chosen to build the Eilat oil line. This canal is one of Israel's unexpected and spectacular sights as it winds for ten miles along rocky hillsides, sometimes many feet above the valley below it. Concrete-lined, it looks like a water-filled scenic highway as it flows past rocky terraces, tree-covered hills, only partially developed areas, and the lush farms of *kibbutzim* and other settlements. The canal bottom and floor are covered with a layer of special earth called *hizriya* and an asphalt membrane. Where streams or surface run-off might flow into the water, drainage ditches intercept them. Wadis are carried across the canal in bridgelike flumes. Specially selected grasses grow alongside the canal to prevent soil from being washed into it by rains.

As if the pumping station were not enough, there are two gigantic siphons built into this stretch of the canal to carry it past deep wadi gorges. At Nahal Amud, an inverted steel pipe siphon takes the water to the bottom of the 450-foot gorge and up the other side. It was installed in 15-foot-deep trenches cut into the sides of the gorge by workmen hanging from ropes. Concrete for flooring under the climbing pipes was carried in by an electrically operated cableway. Fortunately, the second siphon, at Nahal Tsalmon, was simpler to install, because the slopes were easier and the gorge only a third as deep as that at Nahal Amud.

When the canal finally reaches the Nahal Tsalmon Valley, it flows into a reservoir excavated there to build up a water reserve for the second pumping station and to absorb any excess flow caused by heavy rains. The floor and banks of the reservoir were covered with heavy compacted clay 3 feet thick to prevent leakage. The Tsalmon pumping station raises the canal another 345 feet. Built into a cut in the hillside, the pumping station shows only a big front wall to the valleys and mountains that stretch out before it.

From the pumping station, the Carrier, now at its highest level, moves through a half-mile-long tunnel under the hilly range near Eilabun and flows into another canal that runs for more than ten miles through the Beit Netofa Valley. Unlike the Jordan section, which is trapezoidal in shape, this part of the canal has a curved bottom and flows gracefully through the highly cultivated Beit Netofa Valley. At the southern end of the valley, there are two reservoirs, one of which acts as a settling tank to let silt and other matter drop to the bottom. Here, the water is tested and treated chemically if necessary. The other, and larger, reservoir, holds the incoming water for release to the continuation of the Carrier, which becomes a closed 108-inch re-inforced pipeline carrying the water on for some forty-nine miles to connect up with the Yarmuk-Negev system at Rosh Ha'ayin. Made in Israel, at the Yuval Gad works in Ashkelon, the pipes are coated with asphalt and epoxy resin on the outside. They had to be hauled overland from Ashkelon on specially adapted flat-cars to platforms that had been built for their transfer to heavy-duty trucks. Where the pipeline crosses the Jezreel Valley with its high water table, steel pipe protected by plaster on the insides and Gunite on the exterior was substituted for the concrete.

On its way to Ha'ayin, the pipeline goes through three tunnels. The first is one mile long and takes it through the Nazareth hills. The next—Menashe "A"—is four miles long, the longest tunnel ever built in Israel. Because no such tunneling project had ever before been undertaken, men from all over were selected for it and literally learned as they dug. A short distance downstream, the shorter Menashe "B" tunnel was also built. Construction crews working on the National Water Carrier also blocked off several major saline springs which poured into the Kinneret.

The National Water Carrier is integrated into a system that began with the initial regional water supply built by engineer Simha Blass, Israel's first formally designated water planner, around the Mekorot wells earlier sunk near Kefar Hasidim to supply the communities around Haifa. There are twenty-four such regional projects, running from Metualla in the far north into the center of the Negev. Only the Ha'arava-Eilat project, which supplies water to Eilat, Yotvota, Ayalot, Timna, 'En Yahav, Hatsevea, 'En Boqeq, and the Dead Sea Works, is not part of the presently integrated system.

At this point in time, Israel has the water it needs and is only using about 85 per cent of that available. Projections of future yields from existing water supplies, the aquifers, all the storm water that can be captured and stored, and from reclaimed waste water, indicate that the amount of water available by 1975 will be a maximum of 1,400 million cubic meters, and by 1980 1,540 million cubic meters. Add to this 170 million cubic meters of brackish water (which can be used for some agriculture, fish ponds, and many industries) from the Jordan Valley, the Beit Shean region, the coastal plains, and the Negev—and that's all there is. Projections of the water needed for domestic, agricultural, and industrial purposes are more than 1,500 million cubic meters in 1975, between 1,600 and 1,800 million cubic meters in 1980, and well over 2,000 million cubic meters by the year 2000, when the Israeli population is expected to be in the neighborhood of 5 million.

What Happens Then?

While agriculturalists are working to reduce the water needed to raise crops and industries are learning to reuse and recycle water to cut total consumption (one Technion engineer has designed a flush toilet that uses three gallons of water for one purpose and nine for another, which could save millions of gallons daily), Israel's water planners, scientists, and engineers are looking to artificial means of getting more water. There have been promising experiments in increasing the runoff water harvest by planting grass in place of scrub vegetation in uncultivated areas, and work is going on in an effort to control surface water evaporation. The use of brackish waters is being expanded as agricultural experts develop salt-tolerant animal and vegetable species and new methods of leaching and draining the salts from the soil, but, as indicated earlier, this does not represent a major potential source of additional water.

A five-year study conducted by the Hebrew University in conjunction with the Meteorological Service indicated that cloud-seeding, or rain-making, as it is popularly known, seems to produce a substantial rainfall increase. Seeding of clouds with silver iodide crystals has to be done when the upper-air temperature is at certain levels and when there are rain clouds, so the possibilities of this method are limited. Nonetheless, cloud-seeding has been made an official part of the Israeli water supply program. With the tremendous evaporation loss from the Kinneret and improved methods of harvesting the rainfall, even a slight increase in the annual rainfall would go a long way.

Desalination remains the major possibility for additional water for Israel, although this is still a controversial method because of the relatively high costs involved and because funds for development of large-scale plants are not available in Israel at this time. A special report issued by the Prime Minister's office in July, 1969, stated quite bluntly:

> Though much progress may be made . . . in the state of the arts relating to the utilization of water, the gap between water production and water demand is sure to widen. Only nonconventional methods of water production are considered able to close the gap. Although cloud-seeding experiments have proved successful according to statistical analysis, and some progress has been made in the reduction of evaporation from open water surfaces, one cannot, at this juncture, base plans to increase water production on these results. Israel's water economy must therefore rely, as from the middle of the next decade, on large-scale sea water desalination that will form, from then onwards, an integral part of its national water supply system.

As recently as 1967, Israeli water planners were hedging when it came to talking about desalination even though the nation was already heavily involved in research and development in the field, and in one interview Aharon Wiener cautioned about delaying the construction of a proposed large-scale dual-purpose electric and desalination plant at Ashdod, suggesting that opponents would let a rainy season or two lull them into complacency. Just that happened. But the 1969–70 winter was dry, and now the water crisis period is only three to five years off. Right now, at least one hundred Israeli engineers and scientists are actively involved in desalting research and development, at the Technion, at the Negev Institute for Arid Zone Research, at the Weizmann Institute, and at the Hebrew University. There is no lack of electric power to meet the needs of large-scale plants, and atomic energy, too, will be available in the years immediately ahead.

Several years ago, the United States and Israel undertook a joint study of the feasibility of building a 150-million gallons-per-day (GPD) desalination plant at Ashdod. President Lyndon Johnson personally announced this project and talked about the days ahead when water from the seas would make the deserts bloom. Feasibility studies were completed, but the financing was never resolved. At the same time, the United States was planning a comparable installation off the coast of California, but cost factors again intervened, and that project is in the limbo of re-evaluation. Discussions between Israel and the United States are still continuing, and in the 1969 Congress a Foreign Aid bill was passed that included $42 million for a scaled-down Israeli project, a 50-million-GPD plant that would serve as an experimental prototype for U.S. and world development. Even in its reduced size, it would still be the largest such plant ever built.

As this is written, however, the money still has not been made available, and Israel is still looking for the necessary funding.

The 1969 Prime Minister's office report listed the conditions that should exist in a country where such a first, large-scale desalting plant, providing water primarily for agriculture, could be built:

1. The country is ready and able to share the know-how acquired from building the plant with the rest of the world.

2. The inventory of the country's water resources should be complete, and it must be known there are no alternative sources of water.

3. The people must be water conscious, water management practices must be well developed, and agricultural management well advanced.

4. Technically able people must be available who have previous experience in the development of desalting techniques and in the operation and maintenance of desalting plants.

The report stated:

Israel appears to be the ideal country for developing and testing desalting processes because it fulfills all the conditions outlined above. Israel's experience and know-how of desalination methods, its techniques of water management, its agricultural achievements and its wide experience in the development of arid zones will ensure that the introduction of desalted water into the Israeli system will yield a vast amount of useful knowledge on the economic, technical and social consequences of such action. This knowledge will be of great benefit to the world at large.

There are two levels at which Israel needs desalination technology. One is the very basic level of providing more water, which can only come from the sea. The other is the level of making brackish water usable and combating growing salinity in the basic water supply now available. For example, the Ministry of Agriculture has ruled that salinity in the water supply shall not exceed 170 parts per million (ppm) in the north and 250 ppm in the south. Since the integrated system went into operation in 1964, intensive studies have been made of the salt tolerance of citrus fruits, one of Israel's most profitable agricultural exports. These studies indicate it may be necessary to lower the 250-ppm limit in the south. And other fruits like the avocado, another export item, need even purer water. The salinity of the Kinneret is so high that groundwater must be mixed with it along the pipelines before the water can be used. Within the next few years, the mixing in of reclaimed wastes and the increasing salinity of groundwaters caused by fertilizers and pesticides will make this less effective, especially along the coastal plains where intensified utilization is creating a build-up of salts in the coastal aquifer. While steps are being taken to overcome this, the influx of the Dan River region waste waters may counterbalance the present efforts. It is envisaged that it may well be necessary to overcome this creeping salinization by blending in desalted sea water or taking the salts out of the groundwater itself.

In 1959, the State of Israel established a Sea Water Conversion Commission to study the problem and advise the government on the subject. The National Council for Research and Development was assigned to coordinate and administer government-sponsored work in the field.

In 1965, on the recommendation of the Sea Water Conversion Commission, a demonstration multiflash unit, using distillation techniques, was built at Eilat to desalt water from the Red Sea, which, except for the Dead Sea, has the highest totally dissolved solids content of any ocean or sea. The plant was built by an American firm, Baldwin-Lima-Hamilton, but is operated jointly by Mekorot and the Israel Electric Company. It was designed to produce a million gallons of fresh water daily and has—after some highly skilled "tinkering" and experimentation by its operator,

Zadek Ramm, a Bostonian who came to Israel to fight in the War of Liberation and later went to work as an electrical engineer—operated at 105 per cent of rated capacity.

A graduate of Boston's Northeastern University, Ramm was working at the Haifa Power Station when he was asked if he was interested in working in an automated electric power station. "Go down to Eilat for a few weeks," the power company people told him. He's been there well over five years, running and improving the desalination plant.

When the plant first went into operation, there were problems of poor venting, breakdowns, and too much polyphosphate build-up. Ramm undertook five months of experimentation with sulphuric acid and polyelectrolites to fight corrosion, which, he says "was washing the plant out to sea." He also developed special epoxies to use in patching of tubes and stacks. Although he took his last chemistry course in 1945, he says cheerfully, "This is no country for a tunnel vision specialist."

Eventually, he solved the problems. "I had to," he says, scratching a balding head and grinning wearily, "we couldn't afford to shut down. We had to keep it going. This plant was designed to make so much water a year, and we wound up making more."

The unimpressive-looking plant, which stands out against the hillside only because of its orange and white striped smokestack, produces water that is pumped into the Eilat reservoir, where it is mixed with brackish water from the Arava during the summer, when tourists crowd the town and the desert coolers are hard at work in the houses. During the winter, the plant meets all of Eilat's water needs, and now it is being expanded by the addition of another unit captured in the Sinai Desert during the Six-Day War, so that it can provide a total year-round supply.

Ramm is vitally interested in the role desalination could play in the Negev, where there is a large quantity of magnesium sulphate in the underground water. Reverse-osmosis desalination plants are good for dealing with that kind of brackish water, and he feels that ultimately such plants could liberate Eilat from what he calls the "brute-force way of making water."

The Eilat plant has had other problems, too. The de-ionized

water from the desalting plant ate out the cast-iron water pipes in the town, and the piping had to be replaced by Israeli-made pipes using cement, asbestos, and polyethylene.

Ramm is not the only one interested in the role reverse-osmosis technology, which uses pressure to force the salty water through special membranes to separate the salt from the water, can play in the Negev. About twenty-five miles north of Eilat, the Negev Institute for Arid Zone Research has an experimental pilot plant at the Yotvota Kibbutz and Hebrew University experimental farm.

Another Boston area engineer, Chaim Cohen, is in charge of this project. A tall stocky man who looks more like a camp counselor putting some campers through their paces than an engineer supervising his technical staff, he comes down regularly to the odd-looking assembly of tubing and pumps that is expected, when complete, to desalinate 60,000 gallons of Yotvota well water each day. Told that Ramm has said, "All you need for reverse osmosis is an electric supply, a couple of pumps, and a battery of tubes," Cohen laughed and said he wished that's all there was to it.

The Yotvota plant is a rickety-looking collection of vertical tubes, over eighteen feet long, through which the brackish water runs, topped by a valve-studded platform. It was designed by Sidney Loeb, an American chemical engineer and expert in reverse-osmosis technology on a UNESCO assignment to the Negev Institute. It is similar to one now in use at Coalinga, California.

Yotvota is one of the oldest *kibbutzim* in the far south. Its water supply contains 2,300 ppm of dissolved solids, almost ten times the U.S. Public Health Service minimum standard. Part of the salt comes from rare rain storms, which carry salt left in the air by evaporating Red Sea waters. The plant sits in a hollow, with light brown alluvial limestone on one side and basalt hills on the other. There is a children's swimming pool on a hill above the platform on top of the membrane tubes. The area is flanked by barbed-wire fences and floodlights as protection against Arab raiders from the Jordanian mountains of Moab a few thousand yards away.

Shells and rockets aimed at the *kibbutz* have fallen close to the water-making unit.

On one particular day, Cohen and two assistants, Daniel Levy, a chemical engineer from Portugal by way of the Brooklyn Polytechnic Institute, and Joseph Freiman, a Canadian technician, had come down to check on the plant and clean the tubes, which is done by carving a small ball out of sponge rubber and sending it through the 110 tubes to pick up dirt and sludge. If and when it comes out, it is usually covered with iron oxide. This day, the ball didn't come out, and the two younger men were on top of the platform in the blazing sun, opening and closing valves to see where it was stuck. Water rained down through the tubing on the concrete pad below, narrowly missing a *kibbutznik* who had gone to sleep in the shade of the platform. To add to the occasion, a visiting fireman, the venerable chemist and scientist from the Negev Institute, Rudy Bloch, was cheerfully accusing them of wasting water in the desert!

Ignoring the accusations, they found the ball, closed the valves, pressed a couple of switches, and, presto, within a couple of minutes, clear cool water was available. The special membranes for the plant are produced at the Negev Institute according to a formula devised by Loeb. Some of the tubes are fiber glass, from the United States, and the others are Israeli-made aluminum ones.

Although the unit functions simply and needs only a few minutes attention daily from a *kibbutz* member who checks on the production gauges, it does have what Cohen describes as peculiarly Israeli problems. If the electric supply goes off for a few seconds, the plant shuts down. Eventually, someone comes to check, and, if the telephones are working, calls the Negev Institute in Beersheba, more than 100 miles away, and reports that it's not working. Then Cohen has to talk the Institute into letting him take a government car to drive the three hours down to Yotvota to spend a few seconds pushing a switch to turn it back on after a cursory check to make certain everything is all right. (A few days after our meeting, an Arab saboteur cut the power line to Yotvota and Cohen had to come right back down the road through the Arava again.)

Although the unit at Yotvota is experimental, it is also designated by the National Water Commissioner as a standby water supply for the *kibbutz* and the people in the area.

The Negev Institute is involved in operating even larger desalting units in the Negev. These use the electrodialysis-membrane method of separating the salt and water ions. A demonstration plant producing 130,000 GPD is working at the Tseelim agricultural settlement, and has been used to gather experience and data to enable construction of two larger units—each five times as large —at Mash'avei Sadeh, another agricultural settlement. The first of the two units, built as a joint venture of the Israeli Government and the UN Development Fund, was scheduled to go into operation late in 1969. The well water at Mash'avei Sadeh contains 2,250 ppm of totally dissolved solids (TDS), of which 925 ppm are chloride ions. The product water will contain 500 ppm TDS, with 250 ppm of them chloride.

Meanwhile, at the Negev Institute, the Hungarian scientist Francis Korosy, who left Budapest after the revolution in 1956 to join the Physics Department of the Hebrew University and then moved on to the Technion and the Negev Institute, is developing promising new membranes for desalination purposes. A physical chemist with broad experience, he relates his work in Beersheba to such unexpected things as the need for water to grow valuable fruits and flowers for the Israeli export trade. Desalination is a field that works for the future, he comments, as he demonstrates the flexibility of his new membranes.

His particular effort is selecting and improving membranes. He uses polyethylene, which can be converted to all sorts of membrane uses. He tested his prototypes at the Technion and is now proving their worth in the Negev. The membranes he is manufacturing at the Beersheba laboratory are much less brittle—they can be twisted and folded—than those previously used, can be shipped dry, and are much less expensive than others to make and use. They look like brown-orange sheets of plastic and, it is hoped, will become an important Israeli export in addition to being used in the country's desalination technology.

At the other end of the country, Russian-born Abraham Kogan, an aeronautical engineer who earned his undergraduate degree at the Hebrew University and his graduate degrees at Princeton, has come up with what may turn out to be a revolutionary heat-transfer process for large-scale distillation desalting. His, incidentally, is one of eight different projects at the Technion that are related to desalination.

How does an aeronautical engineer get into desalination? Kogan says, "In aeronautics there are a great many disciplines. We work with fluid dynamics and heat-transfer problems. In 1962, I had an idea that seemed promising and might lead to a much more efficient method of desalination." He rubs a hand over his gray crew cut, reminiscing. "I made a few calculations and decided it was worth the trouble to go a little bit further. I got the go-ahead on a small basis, in the laboratory. The first few preliminary tests showed it would work, so now I'm in it with both feet."

His process, an improvement on multistage flash distillation, eliminates the miles and miles of expensive tubing and heats the water to distillation levels by direct contact, using hot pebbles to bring cold brine to distillation temperatures. By eliminating the use of metallic heat-transfer surfaces, the Kogan process will sharply reduce the cost of building a distillation desalting unit and will require much less thermal driving force, so that operating costs will also be reduced.

His method calls for two units, one of which cascades a stream of hot brine through a series of vapor flashing stages, countercurrent to a cold stream of desalted water. Pure vapor flashed off from the brine is cooled by direct contact with the cold stream, so that the brine becomes cooler and the pure water warmer. In the other unit, two columns of fluid transfer the heat added to the desalted water to the brine recycle stream and the sea water make-up stream before they reach the flashing side of the first unit. Heated pebbles in his prototype unit carry the heat to the first unit, then, after cooling, are reheated in the second unit and move back again to the first. For his experimental unit, a Rube Goldberg–like contraption sticking out of the back of a white cement-block building behind the Aeronautical Engineering offices, he uses an assortment of iron, flintstone, and cement pebbles—rejects that he gets inexpensively from Haifa manufacturers.

Kogan's next step, now under way, is the construction of a pilot plant next to the Israel Electric Company powerhouse in Haifa, where the company will provide him with a source of filtered sea water to run through the tubeless columns.

The Israelis also manufacture small vapor compression desalting units. The Israel Desalination Engineering (Zarchin Process) Ltd., a government-owned company, has developed a low temperature aluminum-tube vapor-compression conversion unit for small-scale desalting. This same company had developed direct freezing desalting plants, one of which was working at Eilat until it was no longer needed. The process, developed by engineer Alexander Zarchin while exiled in Siberia, never became a large-scale process because Zarchin could not develop a large enough compressor. However, at least one knowledgeable desalting expert in Israel believes the fault was not with the process but with the failure to write proper metallurgical specifications for the compressor parts and that some day desalination by freezing, which eliminates the cost of heat energy, may be developed into large-scale operations.

One other desalting process is also being experimented with in Israel, in, of all places, a Hebrew University botany laboratory. There, Ben-Zion Ginzburg and his wife, collaborating with Aharon Katchalsky, of the Weizmann Institute, are studying the way in which bacteria and algae from the Dead Sea regulate their salt uptake.

These algae and bacteria are about the only life known to exist in the Dead Sea. They form bright red patches on the sea, sometimes turning the salt evaporating pans a blood-red hue. Put into fresher water, without the salt they are used to, they die. Preliminary studies of the bacteria and algae show that the concentration of salts in their bodies is twice the concentration of that of the Dead Sea itself, and the concentrations of other chemicals greater in much higher proportions. If the mechanism by which these tiny creatures separate the salt ions from the water can be determined, and can be duplicated, it may be possible to use a chemical process rather than electrical or heat energy to evaporate water, and this, too, could prove far less costly than existing methods. Far out as this investigation may seem, it has attracted research funds from the U.S. Office of Saline Water and the Ford Foundation.

It is interesting to note that apparent confirmation of this bacteriological approach to water desalting may be found in the recent announcement that American scientists had successfully used a similar method to remove oil from water.

In addition to all the experimentation with desalination improvements, there is another method of enlarging the agricultural water supply now being tried experimentally in Israel that has great promise. This is runoff inducement. Researchers from the Volcani Institute and the Hebrew University Agricultural Field Crops Faculty have tried a variety of methods in the northern Negev and the rocky Judean Hills. Their goal is to catch as much rainfall as possible and store it for irrigation purposes in the dry season, which in the Negev is most of the time.

The various methods used in the experiments during three successive growing seasons between 1964 and 1967 included: eradication of vegetation; removal of surface stones to reduce rain interception and obstructions to the downhill flow and to allow the soil to crust over; smoothing the land to prevent puddling; compaction of the top layer of soil to reduce its permeability; dispersion of soil colloids to induce self-crusting, which is done by spraying sodium solutions on soil that has the right amount of clay for compaction and dispersion but not enough to cause shrinking and cracking; and impregnating the surface with sealing or binding sprays such as petroleum solutions.

Although there were obvious variations in the results, which depended on the relationship to actual rainfall amounts and the kind of soil concerned, it proved possible to increase the runoff severalfold; in a desert area where there is a season rainfall of ten inches (the northern Negev comes close to this, and in the Judean Hills it is even greater), yields as high as 2 million cubic meters of water may be harvested each season on a 250-acre treated area. Properly done, the experiments show, controlling and increasing the amount of surface runoff on sloping lands can provide a major source of irrigation water.

Leslie Shanan is a tall, slender water engineer who used his experience as a pilot in the South African Air Force to help Israel in its War of Independence. Today he is a consulting engineer working out of a busy office on wide, tree-lined Rothschild Boulevard in Tel Aviv. His office walls are covered with photographs of water towers, irrigation ditches, and the like. Water supply is his pin-up girl. He started his postwar life in Israel in a *kibbutz.*

Around 1950, he became interested in the existence of thousands of acres of desert area covered with gravel mounds about three to nine feet in diameter and as much as three feet high. The Bedouins called them grapevine mounds, so everyone assumed they were connected with the growing of grapes. One theory was that the cold stones cooled the moisture from the air and collected the dew to irrigate vines growing inside the mounds. Another theory was the pragmatic view that the stones had been dug out of the hillsides and replaced with good soil. A third theory was that the stones had been cleared to increase the rate of erosion by letting the topsoil wash down to the bottomlands. He was not alone in his interest. Two others had been trudging the Negev, investigating the mounds. They were Michael Evenari, a German who is a Professor of Botany at the Hebrew University, and Napthali Tadmor of the Field Crops Division of the National and University Institute of Agriculture. The three had been knocking around the desert independently until 1956, when they teamed up to try to prove which of the three theories was correct.

They studied a thousand of the mounds and found they always seemed to be related to farm units in the valley below. They concluded that the mounds were a way of getting more water off the hillsides. By removing the stones from the loess soil, the ancients who piled up the mounds had permitted it to crust and become impermeable to falling rains, thus increasing the rate of runoff into the valley below.

When you consider that, in this part of the Negev, there is an average of sixteen rainy days a year—spread over the period from November to March—and that on only three days is the rainfall more than an inch (there have been violent storms, but they last only five to ten minutes), the mounds indicated that someone had found a way to make the most of very little. Further investigation revealed that this runoff farming in the center of the Negev dated back to the Nabbatean period two thousand years ago, when there was a great deal of rich farming in that part of Palestine.

In 1960, with funds from the Israeli Government, the Rockefeller Foundation, and the Edmund and James de Rothschild Memorial Group, the trio began reconstructing the ancient runoff farm technology, superimposing a modern water distribution system to direct the collected runoff to specific experimental fields. The ancients had used the hillsides as drains for collecting rainwater, which they channeled into elaborate bottomland terraces. This is generally considered taboo in modern farming, which aims at maximum absorption of the rain and minimum runoff.

Evenari, Tadmor, and Shanan reproduced Byzantine farms to study the runoff farming system, one at Shivta and the other near the ruined city of Avdot, which, as a partially reconstructed tourist attraction, now looks down from its high bluff on the scene of fruit trees and crops growing just as they had when the original Avdot was in its heyday.

The Avdot farm is divided into two parts; four acres are associated with a small rainfall-catchment area of about eighty acres, and six acres are tied into a 600-acre runoff catchment. The southern catchment is divided into five strips, each drained by its own channel—the shallow ditches scarcely visible as the bright sunlight burns down on the beige-colored slopes. The original channels were faithfully reconstructed. The other, larger catchment funnels its flow into a single channel, which leads into a concrete channel and pipe distribution system. In the smaller area, the rainwater flows through the old-style channels.

To see the Avdot farm in the midst of barren mountains and empty slopes is to see a miracle for it is the only sign of life around except for the tourists clustering around a fruit juice stand at the entrance to the nearby Avdot village site. The nearest community of any size is the mining town of Mizpe Ramon, though several miles up the road is the Sede Boker Kibbutz where Ben-Gurion lives in retirement. At Avdot, successful modern desert agriculture has produced orchards and fields of crops. In the middle of the summer, one finds sunflowers, spirit grass, fruit and almond trees, and other plants growing at the runoff farms even though the last rain year had only produced a "big flood" in January, when thirty to forty centimeters fell during the month.

The experimental farms have shown that the proportional runoff yield from small catchments is greater than from the larger ones and can reach as high as 15 per cent of the annual rainfall, and that about twenty acres of catchment area is needed for one acre of crop land. Runoff management is the crucial factor, not the crops themselves, for the yields of peaches, apricots, grapes, figs, almonds, and forage were well above those resulting from dry farming and not too far below those of irrigated orchards and fields.

The experimenting trio was also able to build small single-tree runoff farms, using a tiny catchment area and little earthen walls to contain the water. Larger examples of this are seen scattered along the roads through the Negev, where rain and dew running off the highways is channeled into areas surrounded by small earthen walls. The result is unexpected groves of trees growing here and there where one would least expect them. The Bedouins have taken advantage of these "surprise" irrigation areas to plant vegetables among some of the trees.

To gain further knowledge of how floodwaters run through the desert, the Hebrew University's Department of Geography has spread marked and irradiated stones through some of the wadis in the Negev and rigged telemetric instruments and rain gauges that are connected to an electronic control center at Kibbutz Elot outside of Eilat. Whenever the weatherman says rain is expected in the Negev, teams dash by car and plane for the Nahal Yael wadi to note the movement of the marked stones and check the instruments in an effort to learn more about where the water goes during a sudden desert storm. This information can help water planners determine recharge aquifer points and also be used to ward off flood damage and soil erosion.

Hebrew University's runoff project is an international one, part of the UNESCO International Hydrological Decade. It is financed by U.S. funds provided because the only comparable area that can be similarly studied in the United States is Death Valley, which lacks proximity to scientific laboratories and has no local residents interested enough to take care of necessary on-the-spot observations and work. Water, after all, is everybody's business, and very much a part of the world's as well as Israel's technology of necessity.

VI

A Wasp Named Cohen and Other Wonders of Israeli Agriculture

Thou shalt inherit the holy earth as a faithful steward, conserving its resources and productivity from generation to generation. Thou shalt safeguard thy fields from soil erosion, thy living waters from drying up, thy forests from desolation, and protect thy hills from overgrazing by the herds, that thy descendants may have abundance forever. If any shall fail in this stewardship of the land, thy fruitful fields shall become sterile stony ground of wasting gullies, and thy descendants shall decrease and live in poverty or perish from off the face of the earth.— WALTER CLAY LOWDERMILK, *noted soil conservationist and agricultural engineer, broadcasting his "Eleventh Commandment" over Jerusalem radio in 1939.*

While on assignment from FAO to Israel . . . I watched the severe austerity of 1951–54 converted into a practical self-sufficiency in fruits, vegetables, fish, poultry and into surpluses of citrus and other crops for export to pay for imports that could not be grown in Israel. Irrigation was extended each year; swamps were drained, forests were planted, native

and induced grasses were spread over the countryside for livestock . . . Israel has become an instruc-
tive Pilot Project in these matters for the future
development of Israel, as well as for developing
countries of the world.—WALTER CLAY LOWDER-
MILK, *at an American Technion Society conference
in the 1960's*

Efforts to describe food production in Israel defy ordinary limitations of time, space, and imagination. The many plants and
trees described in the Old Testament and the presence of Jaffa
oranges in American supermarkets notwithstanding, the popular
American image of Palestinian agriculture is limited generally to
date palms, olive groves, nomadic sheep-raising, and fishing from
lateen-sailed boats reminiscent of *National Geographic* layouts.
There is much, much more to it.

The nineteenth-century Jewish immigrants began with a once-
fertile land that had been turned to swamp and desert by human
neglect. They fought heat, pestilence, hostility, near starvation,
and their own lack of farming know-how to build a new agricultural homeland. Today, Israeli farmers produce all of the eggs
and vegetables their people need, 97.2 per cent of the dairy products, 96.8 per cent of the fruits, 94.4 per cent of the meat, 92.8
per cent of the potatoes, 90 per cent of the fish. They grow almost
all of the cotton used in the Israeli textile industry. Only cereals
and oils and fats are imported in large quantities. Foodstuffs and
beverages rank first in industrial output, agricultural exports out-
rank, in dollar value, every other category of goods but polished
diamonds, and account for almost 20 per cent of the country's
total export income.

Farming villages—the *kibbutz*, the *moshav*, the small town, the
nahal (small combination military-agricultural outposts in strategic border areas)—numbering more than 700 have been created
in the past two generations, over 480 of them since the State of
Israel was created. The amount of land under cultivation has
increased two and a half times since 1948; the production of
citrus fruits about four times; grapes almost five times; bananas
sixteenfold; wheat more than ten times; hay and fodder production has trebled; potatoes and other vegetables more than four-

fold; poultry-raising has increased by over 1,700 per cent; cattle raising by 1,500 per cent; fish farming sixfold; milk production has grown to five times what it was in 1948, and egg production has almost sextupled. The growing of cotton and sugarbeets, both large-scale crops, did not exist twenty years ago.

These statistics are as much the result of historical necessity as the application of modern agricultural technology and the development of innovative methods of irrigation, pest-control, use of fertilizers, animal-, fish-, and poultry-breeding, and almost instant implementation of the findings of a veritable army of agronomists, microbiologists, plant geneticists, chemists, entomologists, horticulturalists, zoologists, and educated dirt farmers who joined forces to feed the people of Israel.

Picking a point at which to begin this story is a matter of pulling one piece out of a kaleidoscopic pattern of animals, vegetables, and minerals. But a brief historical reminder needs to come first.

After World War II, Israel faced another three years of struggle before it became independent. Ever since, it has been surrounded by the sealed borders of enemy states. The self-determined exodus of Arab residents in 1947 and 1948 took hundreds of thousands of farmers off the land; they were replaced by city-dweller immigrants who had to be taught to farm. There were acute food shortages in the late 1940's and early 1950's, and rationing was prevalent as the new State sought to provide everyone with a minimum diet at a reasonable price. Milk, already low in fat content, was further diluted with dried skimmed milk and water; eggs were given almost exclusively to children; meat was in short supply, and it was not unusual to find donkey or camel meat sold as beef. A decade later, the situation had changed remarkably as the new immigrants learned to take advantage of the fertile, frost-free land on which, with the help of irrigation, they could produce two or three crops a year. Only field crops such as wheat, barley, corn, and soybeans are still limited by the availability of water and arable land; eggs are readily available, and broilers, grown in the 1950's by only one *kibbutz*, are now in all the Israeli supermarkets in plastic-wrapped profusion. If you really want donkey or camel meat, it's hard to find. The first pasteurized milk went on the market in 1955; now fresh milk and dairy products are available even at roadside stands in the desert.

The citrus industry, which went into a relapse during and immediately after World War II, has become one of the nation's biggest exporters. *Shmouti*—the famous Jaffa oranges—are harvested in the frost-free winter along the coast, and spring-ripening Valencias extend the season by several months. Grapefruits and lemons are major export items, along with fruit juices and concentrates. An orange paste, made by pulverizing the entire orange, has become the base for fruit squash drinks in Europe. Apple-growing has increased greatly, especially since Israeli research developed a chemical spray that controls the dormancy of apples and peaches so that they no longer require a period of cold weather to produce fruit.

Israeli agronomists have experimented with more than 5,000 plants from all over the world, to find the species that will thrive in one or more of the country's varied soils and climates. They have bred for salt tolerance to take advantage of the brackish or saline water supply, and for heat- and disease-resistance. To this almost molecule-by-molecule and gene-by-gene study of each plant's growth and reproductive processes, they have added new methods of irrigation and pest- and disease-control. At the same time, engineers and chemists at the Technion and the Weizmann Institute, as well as in government laboratories, have attacked the problems of storage, processing, and containerization to enhance the durability, flavor, and color of produce that is shipped to domestic and overseas markets. The government has brought in modern farm equipment and has developed much of its own to meet the specific needs of its farmers. Much of the agricultural research has been financed by the United Nations, the U.S. Department of Agriculture, and a host of foundations. Still more has been the direct result of work in such Israeli Government laboratories as the Volcani Institute, the Negev Institute for Arid Zone Research, the Agricultural Engineering Institute, the Kimron Veterinary Institute, the Sea Fisheries Research Station, the Fish Culture Research Station, the Laboratory for Research of Fish Diseases, the Soil Erosion Research Station, the Irrigation and Soil Field Service, the Plant Protection Department of the

Ministry of Agriculture (which studies problems of storage, rodent and locust control, and pesticides), the Biological Control Institute, and the Citrus Production Board. Also, of course, there is a wealth of basic and applied research going on at the Hebrew University, Bar Ilon University, the Weizmann Institute, and the Technion. Even troops in the field—including those along the Suez—get involved in some of the food-related research projects.

Hand in hand with all this agricultural research goes the technical advance of the food-processing industry, and in this area the Technion has played a vital role through its various research and development programs, which include everything from guidance in building a processing plant to the setting of standards, studying the practical problems of the farmer and the processor, improving canning, storage, and shipping methods, and devising new equipment for use in the plant and on the farm. Unfortunately, space does not permit a description of the Technion's many innovations in this field, which have been a major contribution toward the agricultural technology of necessity.

Milk and Meat Production

One of agricultural Israel's spectacular successes has been raising the annual milk yield of its cows to an average of over 5,000 liters a head. This is one of the world's highest yields, yet it comes from an area that formerly supported only tough, heat-resistant Arab cattle whose milk was scanty. Careful cross-breeding of these Damascene cows with Dutch animals, and equally careful study of bovine physical processes so that food, exercise, and climate could all be manipulated for maximum output, has made the difference.

The meat yield has been similarly stepped up. When the early settlers arrived, they found the Arabs raising the scrawny Damascene cows for milk and to pull plows. When they had outlived those purposes, they became a source of tough, stringy beef. Animal husbandry expert Amiel Berman, a Rumanian-born senior lecturer at the Hebrew University's Agricultural School in Rehovot, recalls early unsuccessful attempts to import European cattle. Each failure was attributed to the inability of the European animals to adapt to the hot Palestinian climate. But, faced with the tremendous increase in population and the costliness of importing meat, the post-State cattle-breeders tried again, with Dutch stock and then Holstein-Friesian cattle. This time, they were successful and realized that their predecessors' lack of skill and knowledge as breeders was at fault, not the climate. Israeli researchers also found it possible for pure imported breeds to adapt to the climate so long as importation had been preceded by the development of scientific feeding methods, strict veterinary and disease control, and improved field crop production. Israelis have used artificial insemination for selective breeding for many years and have also developed a highly successful beef ranching program by crossing the small local cattle with imported Herefords, Santa Gertrudis, and Brahman bulls, to produce a higher beef output.

Under normal conditions, scientific breeding, feeding, and special care would be enough, given time, to produce such ultimate high milk and meat yields as Israel's cattle are now providing. But in Israel neither time nor economic urgency permitted the normal methodologies. This is where close study of the animals' own physical processes came in.

Originally, it was thought that putting cattle out to pasture in natural pastureland—unsuited to other agriculture—would be the basis for cattle-raising, but, unfortunately, Israel's pasture area could be swallowed up in any one of the large cattle ranges of the American Southwest. Moreover, as Berman points out, animals going out to graze increase their internal heat production; in hot climates, this means that too much potential meat and milk are lost to the cow's own overstimulated caloric production. The heat production of a dairy cow is 7,000 kilocalories per day. A cow producing an average amount of milk has no trouble maintaining normal body heat provided it gets adequate shelter from the sun and the heat of day. But when milk production rises 20 kilograms, heat production doubles. When it rises 40 kilograms, heat production triples. In the Israeli climate, the problem of keeping a high-yield cow's body temperature down to normal thus becomes especially difficult. The Israeli cattle researcher's goal, therefore, was to cut down heat production by reducing the work of eating, rumination, and just plain moving around. Experimentally, pasturing in some cases has been reduced to none at all, with the cows stabled and fed precut food and as much as 70 per cent feed concentrates.

Berman earned his Ph.D. in 1959 at the Hebrew University. His subject was the ventilation of animal shelters to create conditions that would help get rid of the excess heat production.

"People went into breeding for higher sweating rates," he recalls, "but, in Israel, with our high investment per animal, we couldn't afford to wait. We went to work cooling the animals with showers, clipping their hair . . . in other words, we adopted intensive husbandry instead of the genetic approach."

Because a heat-stressed animal loses its appetite, Berman and his associates have been studying animal heat-control behavior for several years in an effort to achieve minimum heat stress and energy loss. They have found that animals are already giving off maximum heat in the early morning hours, in anticipation of the day's warmth, so that appetite declines automatically before the body temperature actually rises. If this characteristic is not inborn but is a Pavlovian-type learned response, then, they believe, the animals can be trained into different behavior patterns. They are now experimenting with lights that signal the rising heat to the animals and poultry so they can reduce their activity.

Heat is a very special problem in the Arava—the Negev Valley —where some of the highest-milk-yield herds of cattle can be found at the Yotvota experimental farm standing almost motionless in specially constructed sheds. Here, where the humidity ranges from 15 to 40 per cent, the heat-energy loss is about 30 per cent, twice that for animals on the more humid coastal plains. What's more, animals in the Arava act cold when the temperatures reach what for those along the shore would be comfort levels.

The experiments at Yotvota exemplify the precise detail with which Israeli agricultural research is conducted. In the summer of 1969, the cows stayed in their shelters until about 4 P.M., the time when the air cools as the sun moves toward the horizon and the mountains of Moab begin their astonishing series of color changes. But scientists are not certain that the cattle have to leave the shelters at all and are experimenting with different types of buildings within which they create microclimates so that over-heated animals can move short distances to cooler locations. They are also looking into how little space can be used to raise a dairy cow or baby beef, to reduce the initial investment in land and water. In effect, they are seeking the highest milk and meat pro-duction per acre and gallon of water, and may ultimately come to using the shelters as concentrated feed lots in which the cattle spend almost all of their time. Some males are now being raised for beef on slatted floor areas of just 2.7 meters.

Awassi sheep, improved by crossbreeding to produce more milk and meat, will continue to graze the land as in Biblical times, but will be found more and more in the larger dry-farming areas, eat-ing plants that require almost no water, or on the natural pas-tures of the north. Because the dry-farming areas of the Arava are so vulnerable to Arab rocket- and shell-fire, Berman says the sheep will "require peace" for free grazing.

Already, the sheep have been the beneficiaries of some extraor-dinary experimentation being carried on by Meir Forti, a member of the Department of Plant Introduction and Ecology at the Negev Institute for Arid Zone Research.

At work in his fields outside Beersheba, Forti looks for all the world like the Hollywood prototype of the sunbrowned *paisan*. The visitor standing with him on a hill near the bustling desert "capital," where the wind makes mournful musical sounds as it blows through specially designed holes in the ultramodern monu-ment to Israel's paratrooper war dead, looks away from the city toward what appear to be small patches of scraggly growth. In the distance, a camel moves across the horizon, and closer in, heavy-duty trucks come from Beersheba factories. But Forti sees only the scraggly patch of growth. It is part of his half-planted forty-acre plot in the middle of the rolling, brown, barren desert. There, on ground baked hard and gullied by runoff from the rare rains, he is experimenting with perennials brought in from many parts of the world where they are known to grow almost without water. The plants, some fifty different species including blue bush and salt bush from Australia and various acacias, are left untended, unirrigated, uncultivated, in free competition with the desert vegetation. The first part of his experiment was to prove they would grow; the second part, now in progress, is to see whether grazing sheep will eat them. During a recent round of grazing experiments in which ten Awassi sheep were given free access to the plots, Forti watched to see what they ate, and how much, to determine the palatability of each species of plant. At least thirteen were well grazed by the sheep, and all thirteen recovered their growth in time for the next grazing season. There is every indication that the project may represent a major opportunity to increase sheep-grazing in the desert areas without drawing on shortening water supplies.

Israel has been able to eliminate most cattle diseases and ward off each influx of hoof-and-mouth disease. Part of the success comes from the speed with which farmers accept and implement new methods and are willing to learn by doing what experts suggest. "In Israel," Berman says, "the researchers service the producers. There is mutual trust and acceptance. We don't have to worry about overcoming old tradition."

The Poultry Industry

Itzhak Lempin is Amiel Berman's counterpart in the poultry field. A short, slender man, he works in a Rehovot office next to a laboratory in which one finds a chicken with two electrodes sticking out of its head. One electrode, Lempin explains, belongs to the Hebrew University, the other to the Volcani Institute.

The Israeli poultry industry is highly developed, largely along American lines. To start with, improved White Leghorns were brought in from the United States, selected on the basis of high egg-output, fertility, shell characteristics, body weight, and viability. For meat, broilers are a cross of the White Leghorn with heavier birds such as the White Rock, the New Hampshire, and the Cornish. Israeli poultry-breeding has now reached such a high level that day-old chicks are exported to many countries, including the United States. When Carl Keren refers to Israeli chicken-runs as "egg factories," he is being exact. Research and applied husbandry have been used to reduce all irrelevant body functions and muscle tensions in the hens, even to the point of mixing tranquilizers in their feed to this end.

In breeding broilers, the Israelis use only the first generation and keep renewing the stock. They are second in the world in the use of artificial insemination techniques. Most of their flocks are raised in cages, not on the floors of the hen houses; modern incubators are used for hatching small chicks. Looking at the chicken with the electrodes used to study reactions to various stimuli, Lempin remembers "when we got our eggs from the Arabs and chickens wandered around barnyards" before World War II. The big industry started with Kfar Menachim, a *kibbutz* between Tel Aviv and Jerusalem on the fringe of the Judean Hills, where Ben Chorin, one of the pioneers of the poultry industry, introduced American-style poultry houses for breeding broilers.

The early poultry-breeders had continual problems with diseases and, until the introduction of climatic controls in hen houses a few years ago, had constant trouble with the heat. Every year, for example, the first *hamseen* (a time when the temperature rises and the humidity drops) would kill many chickens by dehydrating them. Chickens can only regulate their body temperatures to average climates; high heat and *hamseen* humidities are beyond their control for they have no sweat glands. (People have trouble adapting to the *hamseens*, too. Many are sickened by this Middle Eastern weather phenomenon.) Now, however, throughout the Jordan and Beisan valleys and at Eilat and Rehovot, air-conditioning and ventilating systems have been installed in the chicken houses.

With applied climatology joining hands with animal husbandry, the only remaining major problem is feed supply. The biggest problem the Israelis face in chicken and egg production is the cost of feed, most of which is imported. They are experimenting with growing their own and have introduced combinations of soya meal, olive, soy and other vegetable oil by-products, antibiotics and vitamin concentrates, ground feather meal, dry yeast, minerals, and even plaster of Paris (which hardens the eggshells).

One accomplishment of the Israeli poultry industry should delight chopped-chicken-liver enthusiasts the world over. Chicken liver sizes have been increased by 400 per cent. Gastronomically speaking, it is interesting to note, too, that in Israel turkey-farming is relatively rare (their is not the same kind of holiday-related

demand as in the United States) and that, although the latest
methods apply elsewhere in the poultry industry the old-fashioned
European way of force-feeding geese to produce large, fatty livers
for the European *pâté* market is still used.

The story of Brooklyn-born Ben Chorin, often called the father
of the poultry industry, is typically Israeli. He learned about
poultry while shoveling out a hen house in the Catskill Mountains
of New York. In the mid-1930's, when groups of Palestine-bound
New Yorkers practiced farming and communal living in upstate
regions or nearby New Jersey, Chorin joined a group at Liberty,
New York, close to a tuberculosis clinic that had a chicken farm.
When one of the poultrymen took sick, Chorin talked himself into
the job to earn some money for the would-be *kibbutzim*. Eighteen
months later, he was managing the farm and taking Cornell University correspondence courses in poultry-raising.

In May, 1939, he came to Palestine. His group lived on a few
acres of land near Petah Tikvah until they were given land by
the Jewish National Fund. The *kibbutz* at Kfar Menachim was
founded in dangerous territory surrounded by Arabs. He and the
others hired out to contractors building army camps for the
British to earn money to subsist on while their farm took shape.
Although chicken-raising was then considered womens' work,
Chorin wanted to establish a chicken house. When the Jewish
Agency would not accept American methods, he became a shepherd instead. After World War II, when he returned from fighting in the Palmach section of the Haganah, Chorin was finally
allowed to do the physical labor that was too much for the women
running the *kibbutz* chicken house, but he was still not permitted
to introduce large-scale American methods. Then, in 1945, he met
a chicken-farmer named Mike Pack, from Lakehurst, New Jersey,
who had come to Palestine to propose that his methods of growing broilers would provide badly needed animal protein for the
meat-short Palestinians. He, too, was laughed at. Pack and Chorin
met in the Jewish Agency office in Tel Aviv, at a moment when
Pack only wanted advice on how to reach Haifa to get a ship home.
Instead, he spent the next month at Kibbutz Kfar Menachim.

Pack offered to supply Chorin with the basic materials for

modern poultry-farming. He shipped everything needed for the first American-style poultry house at Kfar Menachim. He flew in 10,000 chicks and sent in highly concentrated feed. Chorin was in business. Between them, Chorin recalls, he and Pack broke down the "wall of snobbism." Previously, the Palestine-bred Leghorns had used five pounds of feed to reach a maturity of two-and-a-quarter pounds. Pack's New Hampshires reached four pounds on three pounds of feed. To celebrate and prove his point, Chorin sent sample birds to "all the big shots." From then on, he had a market.

One problem with raising chickens is that genetic potentials for growing meat and laying eggs do not necessarily go together. An egg-layer is good for about 200 to 250 eggs a year; meat birds will do well to lay 140 eggs in eight months. Because it is difficult to tell one from the other, Israeli chickens are moved from the floor of the hen house to cages after about eight months. Those that go on laying eggs are kept, the others sold. Those still producing eggs are kept for breeding purposes. The use of cages makes it possible to keep exact records. Now, Israel grows most of its broilers in cages, and Chorin proudly shows letters from a British expert, who has written, "in your country you must have the greatest experience of any kind in the field of husbandry."

Why this emphasis on animal- and poultry-breeding? The answer is sheer necessity. Helen Rossi Koussewitzky, a Yale Drama School student who came to Israel to join the *kibbutz* at Afokim and who subsequently became women's editor of the *Jerusalem Post*, has vivid memories of the World War II period when she was also Director of Publicity for the British Mandate Government's food ministry.

Isolated from much of the world, Palestine was short of food itself and at the same time had to provide food for the British Middle East command troops. "The British had an arrangement with two Arab brothers who were notorious as smugglers," she recalls. "They would buy up large flocks of sheep in Saudi Arabia and trek them across the desert to the Allenby Bridge at Jericho. Then they would double the agreed-upon price. There was little the British could do, for the alternative was to see even this meager supply of meat vanish in the darkness of Transjordan."

To make up for the lack of meat during that difficult time, she conducted extensive promotion campaigns to substitute beans as protein. (Her experience with these shortages—which continued for many years and which necessitated large-scale importation of beef from Eritrea—put her in opposition to the water engineer who claims Israel should not use water to raise cattle, as discussed in an earlier chapter.) Today, as she does her own marketing in a little butcher shop just off King George V Street in Jerusalem, she has available a variety of beef, lamb, and chicken. Her young grandchildren (to whom this book is dedicated) do not face protein-deficiency diseases; even should circumstances cut off all fish and beef imports, Israel is in a far better position than it was as little as ten years ago. The availability of large supplies of meat, eggs, poultry, and fish within the country has sharply reduced the necessity for buying abroad (a crucial gain for a small nation whose balance-of-trade economics is hurting badly because of the high cost of importing for defense and other needs).

Fish Farming

The third major element in Israel's intensive protein-food-development effort is the fishing industry, which has created a new breed of Jewish fishermen who range the high seas, trawl in the Sea of Galilee, and harvest carp from the hundreds of fish ponds that sparkle in the sunlight in many parts of the country. It has united in a major research effort such diverse scientists as a venerable microbiological chemist, a zoologist who says his greatest moment came when he went fishing in the Suez Canal shortly after the Six-Day War, and a twenty-one-year-old brunette from New York, who is trying to grow organisms so tiny, yet so nutritious, that they can be used to feed the artificially bred small-fry that no longer can live in the polluted estuaries of Israel's few rivers

Israel today raises about 90 per cent of the fish its people consume. One-fifth of the land listed as under cultivation is actually fish ponds, which provide about 20 million pounds of fish annually to a nation with an average per capita consumption of about twenty-two pounds. An additional 3 million pounds are caught in the Kinneret, 8 million in the Mediterranean and the Red Sea, and the remainder by Israel's four-ship fishing fleet, which works the Atlantic waters off Africa. The 1968 report of the Ministry of Agriculture's Department of Fisheries lists a total of 1,378 Israeli fishermen using 151 power-driven boats and 334 rowboats. The country's main fishing ports that year were Acre and Haifa, Tel Aviv–Jaffa, and Eilat, and now there are plans to utilize docking facilities at Ashdod, south of Tel Aviv.

M. Oren, a stocky, curly-haired Yugoslav hydrographer, came to Palestine in 1941, just before his country was occupied by the Germans. In 1952, he joined the Fish Research Center, and today he is Director of the National Sea Fisheries Research Laboratory, which occupies a neat-looking square white building on the busy Haifa waterfront. In the pre-State days, there was some offshore fishing by men from *kibbutzim* located along the coast, and some pond-breeding, which began in the 1930's. Since 1948, Oren says, more modern methods have been introduced and now the breeding of fish and scientific fish-farming have become highly advanced in Israel. Under the pressure of need for protein, a Jewish fishing industry was rapidly created. Most of the young *kibbutzniks*, he recalls, were initially enthusiastic about basic agriculture or fishing, but, as the pull of family life strengthened, they became more and more reluctant to remain with the fishing fleets at sea for extended periods. Finally, the *kibbutzniks* withdrew from deep-sea fishing. Now, it is all done by cooperatives or private fishermen, and even today's small but modern fleet has its troubles holding younger men, many of whom go into Israel's navy or the merchant marine.

Initially, the new nation had plans for a large fleet of trawlers but soon found that the waters of the Mediterranean were relatively poor in fish and could not support a big fleet. (The Aswan Dam, holding back nutritious waters that formerly flowed through the Nile Delta, has further depleted the quality of the Mediterranean sardine catch.) Israel also had big plans for the Red Sea, believing the Gulf of Eilat to be rich in edible fish, but this, too, turned out to be a poor resource. After the Sinai campaign, Israeli fishermen moved farther out into the Red Sea, but still their catches were smaller and of poorer quality than expected.

To overcome these deficiencies, trawlers began going into the Atlantic to bring back herring, hake, tuna, and other fish. At the same time, fishing was intensified in the Kinneret, a rich source of a variety of carp that is good for canning and Saint Peter's fish, which is eaten locally and exported. In the early 1960's, the salt-water grey mullet was introduced into the Kinneret, and, in 1969, some 20,000 artificially bred silver carp, brought to Israel from the Far East in 1966 for breeding purposes, were added to the lake's waters.

Fish ponds were introduced early in the 1930's and, at first, were stocked with carp imported live from Yugoslavia. These were kept in the ponds until they were sold. As fish-breeders from Germany came to Israel, the number of ponds grew until now there are well over 10,000. The fish production per acre of pond in Israel is the greatest in the world; whereas in temperate climates fresh-water fish grow only 180 to 200 days out of the year, in Israel's climate they grow from 300 to 330 days each year. The fish are carefully selected, and the ponds are spray-fertilized to encourage the growth of plankton on which the fish feed. By mixing dissimilar species of different sizes, the Israelis make maximum use of the pond waters, which generally contain rain or brackish water that cannot be used for other agricultural purposes. The fish live and feed at different levels in the ponds, and artificial breeding has reached such a level of proficiency that it is virtually independent of natural cycles. The operation of the ponds has been mechanized, with harvesting done by lowering the water and pumping out the fish. Driving through the Jezreel Valley, one often sees the fish flashing silvery in the sunlight while, nearby, a single operator turns the valves.

Early in the growth of fish pond harvesting, a major problem developed in the form of toxic algae. These algae, *Prymnesium parvuum*, were particularly lethal in brackish waters. Finally, a relatively simple solution was developed by Moshe Shilo of the Department of Microbiological Chemistry at the Hebrew University–Hadassah Medical School in Jerusalem, who found that inexpensive copper-sulphate algicides, combined with stirring up the water, could control and eliminate the dangerous algae. Moscow-born Shilo formerly headed the Laboratory for Research in Fish Diseases, run jointly by the Ministry of Agriculture and the Israel Fishbreeders Association during the early years of fish-pond development.

According to Oren, the biggest innovation has been the introduction of grey mullet to the fish ponds and the Kinneret. A marine fish that lives part of its life in fresh water, the grey mullet can be found in many parts of the world but, until a few years ago, was ignored in Israel. When it was introduced into the Kinneret, it grew to sizes never before experienced. In most parts of the world, the small-fry of the spawning grey mullet grow in estuaries or coastal lagoons and are caught when they grow large enough. Because of pollution in the estuaries, the Israelis had to resort to artificial reproduction, which worked well. However, when the tiny, one-millimeter-long fry began to grow, they needed food. This presented a problem: Numbers like 25 million fry, which is Israel's goal, mean a lot of food.

In a cluttered, jar-lined laboratory in downtown Jerusalem, Dr. David Kahane, a microbiologist with little knowledge of fish, began trying to solve the problem of feeding the small fry. One of his assistants was dark-haired, blue-eyed Theodora Paulsen, a student from the City University of New York who worked at the Woods Hole Oceanographic Institute in Massachusetts before she decided, after touring Israel, to transfer to the Hebrew University. (It took her just two weeks to go back to New York, pick up her formulas and clothes, and return to Jerusalem.) Kahane, too, had been working in the United States when he decided to return to Israel to do practical research. With a brief background of research in fish toxins, he chose to try pioneering in the field of feeding the grey mullet instead of working on foot diseases or screening drugs for tropical diseases—two of the assignments also offered to him.

Dr. Kahane's project attacks the Achilles heel of the fish-breeding industry—what to feed the tiny small fry, whose mouths are so small that they cannot eat the little crustacean eggs on which other baby fish thrive. What he and Theodora Paulsen and others are seeking is a microorganism too small to be seen with the naked eye that is nutritious, tasty, lives at the right level of the sea, and does not move too fast for the grey mullet fry. They can do their research only during the two months of the year when the mullet breed in the sea. On their success may well depend the future of grey-mullet-breeding in Israel.

A Hebrew University zoologist, Heinz Steinitz, was born in Breslau and has been involved with fish problems at the Hebrew University ever since the University added them to the Department of Zoology in the pre-State years. Under his direction, the University recently opened a colorful, modern fish-research laboratory at Eilat on the Red Sea, where systematic investigation of Red Sea fish will be undertaken for the first time on an important scale.

For years, Steinitz and his associates have been studying the Red Sea fish and their migration through the Suez Canal to the Mediterranean on a hit-or-miss basis. These observations have become especially important because the waters of the Bitter Lakes, through which the Canal flows, lost their high salinity, and marine life began moving freely from one end of the Canal to the other. The Egyptians have had a small laboratory in operation, but, Steinitz says, little has been published of their work.

In 1966, the U.S. Government asked the Israelis to initiate a full-scale study of marine migration through the Suez to give the United States some idea of what to expect if and when a new canal is cut through the Isthmus of Panama. Steinitz pointed out that Israeli scientists had no access to the Canal or its outlet to the Mediterranean, the American scientists said the Egyptians were not cooperative, and that's where things sat until the Six-Day War in 1967. Six days later, Steinitz left for Ismailia and, from the 19th to the 21st of June, fished the full length of the Canal, from Suez to Kanterra. On occasion, the men who helped him had to be tied together in the water because of the swift flow. From time to time, others have fished there since, and army reservists occasionally gather specimens when the fighting eases. They have already discovered extensive migration of whole groups of fish and crustaceans.

The Suez fishing trip was the climax of a career that began when Steinitz joined the Zoology Department at the University in 1936 and, among his other duties, became the supervisor of the first fish collection. But even before that, as a young arrival in Israel in 1933, he was involved in food supply problems—as a worker on citrus research at Petah Tikvah, in the field of pest control.

Food and Cash Crops

In citriculture and other crop-growing, the Israelis have also made tremendous strides in building a national food supply and export market. Here, they had a fairly solid foundation on which to build when the new State was formed, but the advances since 1948 are still impressive, as the statistics at the beginning of this chapter indicate. Part of the development was occasioned by the need for changing over from mixed farming to cash crops that would help support financially the doubling and trebling population. The main new industrial crops introduced were cotton, sugarbeet, and ground nuts. Between 1964 and 1969, for example, the cotton-growing acreage almost doubled and the yields rose to one of the highest in the world, even though water consumption for cotton-growing dropped and mechanization reduced the number of man-hours involved.

It would be absolutely impossible to cover the various crop developments in detail, but several of the stories related to them bear telling.

One is about the man who changed the sex life of the cucumber.

Stocky, curly-haired Leipzig-born Ezra Galun came to Palestine as a boy in 1933 and is now an associate professor of plant genetics at the Weizmann Institute. Far from being an ivory-tower basic researcher, Galun has placed himself, through his work, right at the side of the Israeli dirt farmer.

He and his associates are working on improving cucumbers, tomatoes, castor-oil beans, and other plants to make them more resistant to disease and easier to harvest. For example, through genetic breeding, they are creating bush plants in place of the traditional tomato and cucumber vines. Not only are the bushes easier to harvest mechanically, they also markedly increase the yield per acre.

To develop a hybrid cucumber that would grow in small bushes, with only one or two cucumbers per plant, and would not require time-consuming pollination by bees the geneticists started with mutations and bred them into species that would stop growing after they had a certain number of leaves. What they were seeking were 100,000–200,000 plants per acre instead of the 10,000 usually grown. At the same time, they had to keep in mind the necessity for producing cucumbers that would be firm and solid for slicing and pickling. They needed a lot of "femaleness," for a larger number of blossoms, so they had to breed this characteristic into the plants—and then there was the problem of pollination.

"It's just too much for the bees," Galun says, "because you want most of the plants pollinated in two to three days. If you rely on bees, you limit the number of plants you'll have." To solve this problem, he introduced plants of a parthenocarpic character, greenhouse varieties that bear fruit without pollination. When you do this, he adds quietly, "the whole concept of agriculture changes."

But changing the character of the cucumber plants alone is not enough. The ripening of the plants must be coordinated with pickle factory schedules. So, just as Israeli apples are sprayed to regulate their period of dormancy, so also are the new cucumber fields sprayed with chemicals to provide for consecutive ripening. "It's like the assembly line in a car factory," Galun suggests as he describes the sequential planting and spraying.

Comparable work is going on with wheat and other grains, too. Wheat that was used in primitive farming is being grown again, and, among the strains showing promise in marginal areas, are some collected in the Sinai and from Bedouins in the southern Negev in 1956 and 1957. The problem on which the biogeneticists are now working is to bring the ancient wheat's yield and baking qualities to high levels.

"Israelis are highly conscious of bread quality," Galun notes. "Whenever Chaim Weizmann went to the United States, he looked for Jewish bakeries. We just don't find ordinary white bread palatable."

Across the road from the Weizmann Institute is the Hebrew University Agricultural School. There, too, plant pathologists are concerned with improving not only Israel's grain crops, but also the world's. These modern-day Aaronsohns—working with the U.S. Department of Agriculture in the United States and its counterparts in Canada and other countries—are combing the hills and deserts, and now the Sinai, for disease-resistant strains of wheat, barley, and oats that may be thousands of years old but have somehow withstood the ravages of the fungus rusts that diminish the harvest of the world's farmers.

One such plant pathologist is tall, dark Amos Dinoor, who came to Israel from Vienna as an infant before World War II. He has crisscrossed the country from border to border harvesting wild oats, beating his way into the middle of nowhere so many times that, he says, "My driver thought I was a nut." What he and others, including such well-known pathologists as Michael Zohary and Izaac Wahl, have done is to use jeeps and modern conveyances to retrace the path of pioneer Aaronsohn, who tracked down Biblical grains at the turn of the century, in the never ending struggle to find stronger, now old strains to replace the weakening ones presently being grown. Zohary, for instance, found the original wild grasses that combined to form wheat, while Dr. Zev Amitai, a Volcani Institute plant pathologist, located new genes that governed disease resistance in wild wheat and has had some success in transplanting them. Professor Wahl took other wild wheat and barley to Holland and tested these grains in fields of diseased plants, finding some of them highly resistant. Wild barleys these men have located have successfully tested out at the Volcani Institute and in the U.S. Department of Agriculture Research Center in Beltsville, Maryland.

The continuing problem for agriculturists the world over is that disease agents adapt genetically and, one by one, break down new resistant varieties of grains. For example, the vast prairie wheat fields of the United States have long been prey to new pathogens. The only practical solution to this problem is to look for new varieties at the same time plant geneticists, for future breeding purposes, laboriously seek the genes that control disease resistance. In Israel, in the middle of the world's oldest granary, this means looking for ancient wild varieties. The only trouble is that, since, these, too, eventually lose their resistance, the search must go on and on.

Dinoor's specialization is oats. He made himself a grid map of Israel and set out to pick all the oats he could find across the landscape. It took three months to find them and bring them back to his laboratory. Tested at Rehovot, Beltsville, and in Puerto Rico, many of the Israeli strains proved highly resistant, even against diseases the Israelis didn't know about. Moreover, some of the Israeli selections were unusually rich in protein, and now are being bred into regular oat strains to bring about a total enrichment of the oat crops in the United States.

Because Dinoor knows that the disease-resistance breakdown cycle will continue, he is now working with researchers in Jerusalem laboratories to find out just how the wild plants protect themselves against rust. The wild oat is Israel's most prevalent plant. If its secrets can be unlocked, it may help feed all of the people of the world.

Pest control is as vital to Israel's food and cash crops as the development of disease-resistant plants. One of the men most concerned in this field is Israel Cohen, venerable head of the Agrotechnical Division of the Citrus Control Board in Tel Aviv. A pioneer in biological pest control, Cohen is undoubtedly the only Jew in the world who has a wasp named after him. The wasp is from Hong Kong. For several years, *Aphitis Coheni,* its kinsman *Aphitis Holoxathus,* and the common ladybird have been waging a successful war against parisitic infection. Together, they save the Israeli citrus industry from millions of dollars worth of losses annually. The *Coheni* wasp is particularly effective against red scale.

Cohen's story is part of the larger pattern of the growth of the Israeli citrus industry, which got its start on coastal land sold cheaply by the Arabs because they thought it worthless swamp. The industry declined during and immediately after World War II, then began to boom, and now covers 110,000 acres, 20,000 of which are orchards of young trees that have yet to reach maturity. From the original orchards, which stretch for seemingly endless miles along the coastal plains, citrus-growing has spread into the central valleys, where much of the grapefruit does extremely well on the heavier soils, and into the arid Negev where, surprisingly, there is more area used for citrus than in the fertile valleys farther north. Three-quarters of the citrus crop is oranges, the remainder grapefruit, lemons, and the like. The staple Shmouti orange, in particular, does extremely well in Israel, where it has three to four "flashes" of growth, as compared to two to two-and-a-half spurts of growth in Sicily and one-and-a-half in Sardinia.

With citrus ranking as the number one agricultural export— Israel exports more grapefruit than any other country in the world —it is obvious that anything which can be done to protect the crops and improve the yields is of utmost national importance, especially since urbanization of the citrus areas around the coastal plains and the limitations of water supply in the Negev place stringent controls over future expansion of citrus-growing acreage. Dean Shaul Monselise, head of the Hebrew University Faculty of Agriculture and professor of citriculture, a native of Milan, Italy, sees strong parallels to California, where water limitations and urbanization are also hemming in the citrus groves. But, he notes, Israel's climate gives the country definite advantages over both California and Florida, because there is virtually no frost hazard in the Israeli citrus belts and the climate is such that orange or grapefruit trees can grow side by side with almost any kind of fruit tree that grows in the temperate or tropical parts of the earth. The Israelis can—and do—mix apples and oranges, and cotton and oranges, and peaches and grapes and olives.

One major difficulty facing citrus-growers, especially in the Negev, is the salinity of the water supply. Citrus trees are especially susceptible to salts, and the water coming through the National Water Carrier to the Negev groves is of borderline tolerance. Better use of water plus improved irrigation methods have helped solve this problem to some extent, but intensive investigation of mutant rootstocks with higher salt tolerances is now going on. It is perhaps indicative of the faith one discipline has in another in Israel that the citrus groves were planted in the Negev three years before the pipeline got there. The growers had enough water available for young trees but not enough for active, fruit-bearing ones. If the pipeline had not been completed in time, the groves would have been lost. "Only a crazy country like Israel would plant citrus groves three years ahead of the water supply," Dean Monselise says with a broad grin.

Another problem for the growers was that many areas they were developing were infested with Bermuda grass, a weed that is particularly harmful to citrus groves. The Jewish Agency had to decide whether to start the young trees and hope that Monselise would come through with the right weed-killer in time. It was a risk, but again necessity ruled, and he did come through. The weed-killer that proved most effective, and was used on a large scale first in Israel, was an American chemical product called Bromacil, a systemic herbicide that entered the roots of the grass from the soil and literally burned up the plant underground.

Because of Israel Cohen's work with wasps, begun in 1954, the virulent California red scale has all but disappeared in the older citrus groves where the Hong Kong wasps that Cohen brought in laid their eggs and the larvae ate up the scale. But in spite of this success with biological pest control and earlier successes with another parasite brought in from Japan in 1940 to control another important citrus pest, still other pests for a time threatened to destroy much of the citrus crop. The worst threat came from "black scale," with Mediterranean fruit flies and rust mites ranking next.

To combat these new attackers, Cohen and others at the Citrus Board had to overcome many problems—among them a shortage of young entomologists to work on biological-control methods and the need for research and for teaching farmers to use selective chemicals to avoid destruction of the wasps and other parasites "working" in the citrus groves. For example, air spraying of cotton fields with DDT or other chemicals had to be stopped unless the cotton fields were more than 250 yards from the nearest orange grove. The Board's intensive work has resulted in a balanced program of biological and selective chemical controls, which permits the maximum use of irrigated land to continue.

Professor Paul de Bach of the University of California, one of the foremost men in the field of biological pest control, credits Israel with two out of the nine total parasite successes achieved in the past century. Both have come in the citrus industry. One of them is the introduction of the Japanese *Clausenia Purpurea Ishii*, the other the wasp from Hong Kong named Cohen. However, if any one researcher in Israel could be called the grand old man of pest control, it would probably be sixty-three-year-old Aharon Shulov, who parlayed a boyhood experience of lying in the fields near Kirovograd in Russia listening to the sounds of the grasshoppers and wondering how they were made into a unique method of locust control. This gentle, balding scientist operates out of both a Hebrew University office in a former monastery overlooking busy modern Jerusalem and a Biblical-looking zoo he runs on a rocky Jerusalem hillside within artillery range of the former Jordanian border. In addition to his work in locust control, he has developed the world's most effective serum for scorpion bites and an extremely effective method for combating the kharpa beetle, which infests stored grain. On a typical day, Shulov will devote part of his morning and early afternoon to milking venom from scorpions and watching his associates jam the sound waves of caged locusts, and then go on to his zoo— where he sings to the monkeys in Russian-accented Hebrew. Both his appearance and his dashing way of driving his little car through Jerusalem traffic come as an odd contrast to the titles of some of his many publications ("Electrophoretic Patterns of the Venoms of Six Species of Israeli Scorpions," "Breeding of the Kharpa Beetle *Trogoderma Granarium Everts* On a Diet of Minced Larvae of the Same Species," and so on).

Shulov works in an office on the second floor of the old Terra Sancta monastery, one of the buildings the Hebrew University took over after it was forced off Mount Scopus in 1947. From his building, one can see the Supersol supermarket, a modern hotel, and the mosquelike tower of the YMCA near the King David Hotel. On the walls of his office, which is cluttered with the usual paraphernalia of a zoological laboratory, are mounted butterflies and a photo of a child on an elephant.

In his younger days, Shulov commanded the Haganah group that dealt with preparations for an air force and he flew small planes to "dive bomb" malaria with insecticides in swampy areas. In 1969, with all of his research projects filling room after room in the old monastery, he still found time each day to wander around his zoo, his hazel eyes peering out from under a Texas-style fedora, as he supervised everything that goes on there.

His work with scorpions began thirty-one years ago, not long after he came to Palestine and joined the staff of the University. "Two small children were killed by scorpions, one near Jerusalem and the other in the Jezreel Valley. This started me in the research," he recalls. Later, in 1955, when he was nearing completion of the project, an eighteen-month-old boy was brought to the Hebrew University–Hadassah Hospital in Jerusalem in agonizing pain following a scorpion sting. Professor Saul Adler, who started the Institute of Microbiology and whom Shulov calls the father of the project, persuaded him to rush to the aid of the boy. "I arrived at the hospital with forty live scorpions, whose blood I 'milked' on the spot. I had nurses inject this liquid, with its neutralizing effect, into the small patient, and his life was saved."

Shulov's breakthrough came when he used pure venom by direct bites into donkeys and other animals that had first been immunized over a period of a year with small doses of dried scorpion venom. Today, blood extracted from the immunized laboratory animals is used as an effective serum; each donkey may yield as many as 800 doses at one time without suffering any harm. This serum is now being distributed by the World Health Organization around the world, including Arab countries where scorpions are a serious problem. Shulov gets his scorpions by prowling Jerusalem and its environs at night with an infrared light looking for them. The life-saving donkeys are kept at his zoo.

Shulov's serum research is not directly related to agriculture, although farmers are often victims of scorpion bites, but his other work in entomology is—especially that with locusts. There is a locust warning telephone number listed in Israeli phone books. Locusts don't breed in Israel any more, but they do come in. Shulov recalls a major invasion of the Jordan Valley in 1929 and 1930, when big trenches were dug and covered with iron sheets to trap the locusts, so they could be chemically destroyed. This technique didn't work fast enough, for it still gave the adults time to lay eggs in the soil. In 1945 and 1946, there was another locust invasion, this time on the coastal plains near Afokim and Natanya. Again mechanical control and poisons were used, but not fast enough to prevent egg-laying. Today, locust scouts keep watch and report by radio, and a task force with vehicles and insecticides is able to destroy the locusts in the night before they destroy the crops and lay their eggs.

It was during the wartime locust invasion that Shulov became aware of the reaction of locusts to one another's sounds. He undertook a long study of the relationship between the sounds and optical and olfactory responses. Years of experimentation enabled him to break down the sounds into those which affected various aspects of locust behavior—breeding, laying eggs, and eating. Now, in his laboratories, associates playing tape recordings of selected locust sounds at caged specimens have been able to stop them from mating, from eating, and from laying eggs. The U.S. Department of Agriculture, which has supported much of this research, envisions the day when low-flying helicopters can use psychological-warfare loudspeakers to stop swarms of locusts from eating and laying eggs. This method will be particularly advantageous, Shulov says, in many countries where the whole locust is pulverized and used for protein.

The kharpa beetle story is another example of Shulov's ingenious research directly applicable to saving crops. As early as 1938, the Ein Harod Kibbutz discovered a heavy infestation of the beetles in stored grain. This is potentially a serious problem; in India, for example, as much as a quarter of all stored grain is destroyed by these insects. One of Shulov's first papers on the subject was published in India, where it was read by American agricultural experts. As a result, the U.S. Department of Agriculture underwrote research that led ultimately to the production of a synthetic repellent based on scents excreted by the beetles, which, it is hoped, will replace DDT and other dangerous chemicals in treatment of stored grain.

The achievements of Hebrew University researchers combined with improved marketing processes in very recent years have created one of the newest and fastest growing agricultural industries in Israel. The export value of flowers grew from less than $100,000 in 1965–66 to almost $6 million for the season of 1969–70. The man who is the country's leading pioneer in the development of cut flowers is Abraham Halevy, a *sabra* (which, literally translated, means cactus, tough on the outside, soft on the inside), born in Tel Aviv and educated at the Hebrew University. He has also worked at the U.S. Department of Agriculture Research Station in Beltsville, Maryland, and been a visiting professor at Michigan State. He is now an associate professor of floriculture at the Hebrew University's School of Agriculture.

What Halevy and his associates have done is to change the life cycle of several Israeli flowers, so that they can be exported at a time when demand is high and local flowers are not available in many European countries. His number one "product" is roses, with gladioli, gerbera, iris, anemones, carnations, and chrysanthemums making up the rest of the exports. Most of the Christmas flowers seen in Western Europe come from the Holy Land.

Horticulturally, Israel has a great advantage. Its widely differing climatic regions offer an unusually rich flora—some 2,500 different flowers as compared to 1,500 in England. Working in this helpful milieu and well supported by the Ministry of Agriculture, Halevy and his fellow scientists have worked out ways of controlling the flowering and production time of important flowers to suit overseas markets. For example, they switched roses over from the natural summer flowering season to the October–May period, with the accent on quality and large buds with desirable colors. They have learned exactly what temperatures and light conditions should be applied to different types of flowers. Now they are working on learning exactly when to cut flowers and how to treat them before shipment and have developed a chemical solution that ensures a good "opening" and greater longevity, which will become one of the products marketed worldwide by the Dead Sea Works in the near future.

Halevy was a soldier in the Negev Brigade during the War of Independence. He stayed at the religious *kibbutz* of Sa'ad near the Gaza Strip. Decades later, the *kibbutz* began growing flowers but, for religious reasons, could not cut them on the Sabbath. They turned to their old friend of the war years for advice. He developed a special chemical mixture for the Sa'ad roses; the *kibbutzniks* now cut the flowers on Friday afternoon before the Sabbath, and put them in a chemical bath until the end of the Sabbath the following evening. Approximately 15 per cent of Sa'ad's floral output was thus saved, but more important, it was found that the "Sabbath solution" bath preserved the flowers better than if they had remained in a natural condition. Now, all Sa'ad flowers are cut early and bathed in the solution before being flown to the overseas markets.

Raising flowers seems an odd act of necessity. But Israeli horticulture is becoming so important an export industry that growers are talking of buying their own jet airplanes to transport fresh cut flowers to European winter markets.

Farming and Water Use

Inevitably, many of the areas of Israeli scientific and engineering development overlap. Probably chief among these are water and agricultural research. Research in the efficient use of water for and in agriculture has been of paramount importance in Israel. During 1966–67 alone, there were thirty-two such research projects ranging from the water requirements of alfalfa in the Hula Valley and avocados in the western Galilee, to testing the salinity of field crops in the northwestern Negev. Projects included testing optimal irrigation methods for flowers being grown under glass or the ubiquitous polyethylene-sheeted hothouses (seen by the thousands throughout Israel) and the drainage of fine-textured soils.

One of the more spectacular successes, already in use on over 2,000 acres, was originally designed by the veteran Israeli water engineer, Simha Blass, and proven out at the Hebrew University experimental farm at Yotvota by Dan Goldberg, head of the Agricultural School's Irrigation Department, and M. Shmueli, head of the Soil-Water Laboratory at Yotvota.

The idea is basically simple: It is trickle irrigation, by a system of perforated plastic pipes laid on top of the ground and designed to provide just the right amount of water needed at any given time. In addition, the water flows through a liquid fertilizer supply and thus carries food along with water to the plants.

Originally, trickle irrigation was designed as an underground system, but the holes in the plastic pipes plugged up. Pipes lying on the surface of the ground and watering the soil directly proved to use a minimum of water and avoid most of the feared loss by evaporation that was—and is—the major drawback of the wide-spread sprinkler irrigation systems now in use throughout Israel. The area in which the new technique has proven most successful is in the southern Arava, where there is little water and rainfall and the sand is windblown, salty, and highly variable. Before the ground could be used, it was thoroughly leached with brackish underground water supplies. The shifting dunes were only roughly leveled.

Once the trickle system is installed, nozzles discharge the water gently along the length of the plant row. Sensors indicate when the soil has dried to the point that more water is needed, so there is not a continuous flow of water. The results of these experiments showed excellent yields of tomatoes, cucumbers, melons, peppers, and sweet corn in a part of the desert where only indigenous bush had grown for years. And the yields were far greater than those from sprinkler irrigation. Even relatively saline water produced more tomatoes through trickle irrigation than by use of sprinklers. One immediate result of the experiment is that both the *kibbutz* at Yotvota and a nearby Nahal output are now growing melons and selling them commercially with great success.

Because it permits regulation of water and fertilizer to the specific needs of each plant or field, trickle irrigation holds great potential for Israeli agriculture, which is now entering a period when water supply alone may hold back its expansion in the face of a growing need to feed more people. Dan Goldberg calls the trickling system another "philosophy of irrigation," proved out at his "university in the desert." To Israel's Negev farmer, however, the result is far more practical than philosophic. Ultimately, it may be the key to the old Zionist dream of making the desert bloom.

VII

Mining the Dead Sea

At the time when Novemeysky began probing the Dead Sea, Rutenberg's linemen slung their first high-tension lines across the northern valleys, and Wilbush was expanding the Shemen Oil factories in Haifa, few people would have forecast the industrialization of Palestine. Jewish settlement was envisioned by the Zionists as a return to the land and little more.

Until the State of Israel was created, there was scant industrial growth. The Dead Sea Works—first called the Palestine Potash Company—were unique, but their production was far from noteworthy. Most industry was related to food-processing, with the major exception of the diamond-polishing done by the Yemenites at Natanya. There were no industrial plants suitable for swift conversion to a war effort, and the new State, with its back to a military wall, had to depend upon improvisation and smuggling for urgently needed arms production.

Israel in 1970 still has no Pittsburghs, Detroits, or Bremerhavens, no great clusters of factories of rows of blast furnaces that light up the night (if you look sharp from atop Mount Carmel, you might see one or two), no endless rows of chemical and oil plants such as those one passes going north through New Jersey. There is only one "minepatch" community in the whole country, Mizpe Ramon near the great Maktesh Ramon crater in the central Negev. Only one small cluster of oil derricks rises near Ashkelon, where the Heletz oil field was discovered in 1955. If you put the Israeli shipyards down next to those on the Brooklyn or Chester, Pennsylvania's, waterfronts you'd hardly notice them, except for the fact that they are so much cleaner and brighter. The Bedek aviation plant at Lod is the only really big factory in the whole country.

Yet Israel *is* rapidly becoming an industrial nation; in 1967, industrial exports were five times agricultural exports. From 1950 to 1966, industrial output rose fivefold and industrial employment grew from 89,000 to 220,000. In actual output, the food and beverage industries rank first, metals and machinery second, textiles and clothing third, chemicals and petroleum products fourth.

Much of this industrial growth reflects growing consumer demand and the building and construction that is going on in Israel. It also reflects increased use of the country's few natural resources and, in the aviation and shipbuilding fields, the development of whole new technologies to meet important national needs. This industrial growth, an important key to the future economic viability of Israel, also represents the country's uniquely integrated national planning, for it involves resettlement of immigrants, creation of new communities centered around industrial employment, and the fullest utilization of Israeli science and engineering talent.

Nowhere is this more evident than in the field of chemical and petrochemical industrial development. Here again, the way in which the Israelis can build from an unexpected natural resource, the Dead Sea, is a classic example of the technology of *ein breira*. This small body of "dead" water is meeting not only many of the country's internal needs but also provides the natural resources for a tremendously important export industry.

Novemeysky's hard-won concession to exploit the mineral content of the Dead Sea through solar evaporation had some success in the years before the State was created. In 1931, the first marketable quantities of potash were produced, and, by World War II the Palestine Potash Company was able to turn out almost half the needs of the English and 80 per cent of those of the British dominions. By 1947, production at Kallia, at the northern end of the Dead Sea, and at Sdom, at the southern end, totaled 102,000 tons.

After the War of Independence, the Arabs occupied Kallia and destroyed the Works. During the war, the Sdom plant was cut off from other Jewish settlements. The workers there held out, hungry and thirsty, until the siege was lifted by the Israel Defense Forces. Sdom remained in Israeli hands, but many problems had to be solved before production could be resumed. The plant was isolated by poor roads, and most of the land used for evaporation ponds was in Jordanian hands.

During the first years after 1948, work at Sdom was largely research, headed by Moshe Langotski, who had come to Palestine from Siberia with Novemeysky. Other studies were carried on in the Hebrew University laboratories in Jerusalem. The story of the Dead Sea Works' revival and growth really begins with the building of the "impossible road," without which the Sea's products could not be moved to processing plants or shipping ports. Also involved are the discovery of natural gas fields, prospecting for fresh water, the building of a chemical industry, and a great deal of scientific and engineering ingenuity.

The only trails leading to Sdom were old winding caravan routes designed for camels, not trailer trucks, and even these had long since deteriorated. It took eight hours to get there from Jerusalem in a four-wheel-drive jeep. The ruins of Roman fortresses guarding the approaches to Sdom and Masada had little to watch over except soldiers on maneuvers, an occasional scientific expedition, intrepid tourists, or the handful of workers and scientists who joined forces to keep the developmental work alive against the day when production facilities could be expanded and work resumed.

Construction of the impossible road began in 1951 and was completed in 1953. It was supervised by Technion-educated engineer Ephraim Lotan, whose major experience had been roadbuilding in the gentler valleys and slopes of the north prior to being assigned by the Ministry of Public Works as Chief Engineer for the Negev District.

The new road was built through rough, rugged badlands, largely unexplored, where there had never been a road before.

The original plan was to make the descent from the mountains to the water—a quarter of a mile below sea level—with seven large hairpin turns, but, on one photogrammetric aerial survey, Lotan's engineers found a canyon that appeared on none of their maps. Lowering their tools by rope and climbing the canyon walls with rope ladders, they decided it was possible to build the road right along the canyon's wall.

Heavy-duty trucks, buses carrying workers and tourists, and private cars now pass easily over the road, which was blasted and chiseled out of the northern side of the canyon, a vertical cliff down which ancient waters once cascaded in a straight fall into the Wadi Arava. At the point where the road turns north for the descent into the gorge, there is a magnificent view of the Wadi Arava, the Sea, and the Mountains of Moab in the Jordanian distance.

Before it was finished, parts of the new Beersheba-Sdom road were blasted through soft rock hills and had to cross stretches of salty sand that couldn't bear the weight of a man. Blasting took the road through soft stone, while chiseling with pneumatic drills hacked it into the steep Nakb Jochenia Mountains. Gradients were frequently so steep that additional zigzags had to be carved out of dangerous slopes so that heavy compressors and bulldozers could be moved. In the Wadi Fukrah, where sporadic winter rains pour down in torrents, special embankments were built to protect the work crews. Yet the mountain-spanning problems were far from the worst. To facilitate crossing the soft salt soil approaching Sdom, thousands of tons of muck had to be carted away and replaced with gravel hauled from the wadi beds so that the road could hold the expected traffic.

There were human problems, too. The work force was beset by Arab marauders. New immigrants were not used to doing heavy manual labor in the terrible heat and were homesick for their families (they had to live for weeks on end in tent work camps along the route). When local water sources dried up in May, drinking water had to be hauled in from long distances.

Despite the hardships and difficulties, in January, 1953, the first jeeps and military vehicles traveled the fifty-one miles from Beersheba. Waiting for them was Langotski, who, with his small band of watchmen, had lived in voluntary "exile" for almost five years. On March 27, the road was fully paved. At the dedication ceremonies, conducted under an archway on which were the words of Isaiah, "and the desert shall rejoice and blossom as the rest . . . and a highway shall be there," Prime Minister Ben-Gurion said, "This is the most extraordinary road in the world." He drew a parallel with the road built by Israeli engineers to lift the siege of Jerusalem in 1948: "As the opening up of the 'Burma Road' was the climax to our struggle against human enemies, so the construction of this road forms a climax again in our struggle against nature."

Since that day, additional roads have been built north along the shore to the Kibbutz Ein Gedi and linking Sdom more directly with the ports of Eilat and Ashdod. Israeli roadbuilders are gradually crisscrossing the Negev with highways to open up pathways for settlement, mineral exploitation, and the rapidly growing chemical industry. The bulldozer is helping the Negev gain new life from a dead body of water.

One of those who played an important role in the development of the Dead Sea Works is sixty-eight-year-old Moshe Rudolph Bloch, a German-born physical chemist who was working on the supercooling of water when his experiments were interrupted by the Nazis. It is typical of Israeli science that the three men who played such key roles in mining the overheated waters of the Dead Sea were Novemeysky and Langotski from the frozen gold fields of Siberia and a German chemist who had been specializing in refrigeration before he went to work with the Palestine Potash Company in 1936. Bloch, incidentally, retired from the Dead Sea Works in 1968 but still serves as a consultant to the company and, among other activities, is Chairman of the Scientific Board of the Negev Institute of Arid Zone Research in Beersheba, where he lives. Bloch remembers when the only workers he could find were a handful of *kibbutzniks.* "It was really a scientific, uneconomic proposition, but now it pays as much on capital investment as a forest does."

Potash is one of the world's most important fertilizers, but it is not particularly needed in arid zones such as Israel except for the production of other chemicals, so production, expected to pass the million-ton mark in 1970, is primarily for the export trade. Many valuable by-products are also being produced, ranging all the way from bromine—a basic ingredient of ethyl gasoline, some pesticides, and photographic chemicals—to chemicals that can be used to produce fertilizers and to replace expensive, imported chlorine. The Works also produce a fine industrial salt, the special flower-treating chemicals described in the previous chapter, and, it is generally assumed, a limited supply of uranium for the Israeli reactors.

The Dead Sea Works would have paid off faster had it not been for what Bloch calls "vicissitudes." He views the building of the road as of key strategic and economic importance to Israel. The solar-evaporation process used to extract potash from the Dead Sea is basically simple, for nature does most of the work. The Works present an astonishing vista of seemingly endless fields of white or colored carnallite sludge and vast still pools of bright green or reddish waters, all crisscrossed by pipelines, dikes, and pumping systems. Dredges equipped with spindly equipment move slowly along, pumping the carnallite—the white sludge remaining after the sun has dried up the water—into pipelines for movement to the processing plants on the shore. The Dead Sea is the only place in the world where fractionated crystallization is measured in square miles. When Novemeysky began planning his large evaporation pans, he had only the example of the unchanging, thousand-year-old salt industry to follow, but, at the Dead Sea, controls have been developed to an amazingly fine point when one considers that, even in the intense heat and sunlight of the Dead Sea environs, the evaporation process may take as long as two years.

When it was found that bromine could be extracted from the sludge remaining after the potash had been taken out, Novemeysky was stymied by the fact that one American company extracting bromine from the ocean had a virtual monopoly on the world market. Blocked out of the gasoline market, the Israelis worked with scientists at the Hebrew University and the Volcani Institute to create bromine compounds that could be used as pesticides. During World War II, the pesticide production was given to the Allied Middle East Command. More than 2,000 tons of bromine were produced for the war effort. But, immediately after World War II and the War of Independence, with the plant closed down by "vicissitudes," the American company took over the pesticide market, too. When Bloch and others pushed for resumption of bromine production in the 1950's, they were told they were crazy, but today the Dead Sea Works produces 12,000 tons of the chemical annually and has a potential market for even more. A processing plant has been built in Beersheba to produce and market the pesticides.

Solar evaporation has its own problems. One is its slowness, which Bloch helped counteract by experimenting with different-colored dyes that would speed the heat absorption of the water. He finally selected naftel green as the most effective. This dye adds to the color scheme of the vast evaporation area: At some points, the algae in the water turn the ponds a bright red; other parts, depending on the stage of the evaporation in a particular pan, are green; the large sections in which there is just carnallite sludge look like a snow-covered lake, strangely out of place in the 100°F. heat. Another problem is getting rid of the residual salt in the evaporating pans. One simple solution is to wash it out with water, back into the Sea, but where does one get fresh water at the Dead Sea? Bloch went to Leo Picard, the groundwater-seeking geologist and said, "Nature can't be so anti-Semitic that groundwater runs only to the Mediterranean. There must be some groundwater around here." Around here meant the eroded landscape in which salt- and chalk-columns (one is Lot's wife) rise to the mountain tops. Picard predicted that any water he found would be salty, but he drilled twelve wells. The water was salty, but still "fresh" by Dead Sea standards. Later, a small electrodialysis desalination unit was installed to make it usable for drinking, cooking, and washing.

Not all the salt is being washed back into the Dead Sea. Bloch maintains that the pure salt being refined from the Dead Sea waters is the best in the world; more than 12,000 tons are sold annually. And, after years of experiments, it was found possible to convert the pure salt into magnesium chloride, which, when combined with the ground phosphates found in large supply in the Negev, can be used to produce an excellent concentrated fertilizer. Austrian investors have agreed to finance construction of a plant to produce the magnesium chloride. They will also extract magnesium oxide, an important ingredient of refractory bricks used in industrial ovens. A pipeline is being built from the Dead Sea Works to the new chemical plants at Arad, high in the hills above the Sea. The rich brine will be carried from 1,300 feet below sea level to the factory, which is 2,000 feet above sea level. The end product, produced by combining hydrochloric acid made from the magnesium chloride with the ground phosphates, will be phosphoric acid, a new form of fertilizer, for export.

Expansion of the processing facilities at the Dead Sea itself was enhanced by the discovery of natural gas wells at Arad and Zohar. This gas is piped down to the Sea in another linkup of natural resources in an apparently useless part of the world.

But perhaps the biggest triumph at the Dead Sea is the expansion of the evaporation area itself through the "Gideon Project." Originally, all of the potash came from about 5,000 square feet of evaporation ponds built in flatlands and marshes around the shore. By utilizing all the lagoon and floodable land area not occupied by the Arabs, the Dea Sea Works at Sdom were able to develop only about 11.6 square miles for evaporation purposes. The Israelis hired a Dutch firm, experienced in diking the lowlands, to build a series of dikes that would block off the shallow part of the Sea. A crash program was undertaken in 1962, with three American firms undertaking the actual construction. They had to bring in equipment to shift 10 million cubic meters of earth and stones to build the dikes. Giant dredges were laboriously hauled across Israel from the seaports. The only thing the builders didn't have to supply was the raw materials for the dikes, for the earth and stone were found at Shafek Zohar and moved from the wadi to the Sea on a moving belt more than a mile long that worked around the clock. The total area of evaporation pans built into the Sea itself is now over 31 square miles, as compared to the 5,000 square feet that Novemeysky used. A large, electronically controlled plant, built to handle the increased volume, produces well over 1,000 tons of potash daily.

Along with technical accomplishment of an extraordinary nature, there were also problems of people to be solved in the mining of the Dead Sea. Originally, many young workers were attracted to Sdom by the spirit of adventure and high wages. But they did not stay long in the terrible heat. The work camp took on the aspects of a gold-rush boom town in the western United States or Alaska, with flourishing prostitution and other vices. For a while, Sdom seemed to be reverting to Biblical type. The answer was to build housing for the workers at Dimona, to establish social and educational programs, and to employ carefully selected family men. In the late 1960's, a high degree of selectivity was possible; when eighty new workers were to be added to the 750-man work force, there were 1,000 applicants.

While Rudy Bloch, who might be called the father of mineral-extraction research in Israel, still seeks new ways of improving the products of the Dead Sea (and works on a book that describes the social history of salt), Amos Bunin, a young soil expert at the Hebrew University Agricultural School, is taking Israeli dirt apart molecule by molecule and seeking to develop new uses for a Negev mineral resource with the imposing name moltmorillonite. This substance, Bunin believes, can help prevent the deterioration of heavy agricultural soils in the north.

Bunin grew up in an agricultural settlement between Jerusalem and Ramallah, where the Callandria Airport (formerly Jordanian) is located. He watched "Israel move from mediaeval farming to the twenty-first century," he says, and is now using his laboratory microscope to protect and enhance those gains. His work with moltmorillonite and his intensive studies of soil mechanics are aimed at delaying or preventing the degrading of agricultural soils and reclaiming soil that is already spoiled by overuse and compacting through constant treatment with irrigation, fertilizers, and farm machinery.

His studies are concentrating on learning to control the surface quality of Israeli soil to prevent it from losing its porosity and choking off plants growing in fields and orchards. Mixing moltmorillonite with the soil may be one answer. The mineral, which may also prove of value in making osmotic membranes for various desalination processes, is widely used in the United States. Bunin says that it is available "by the truckload" in the Maktesh Ramon, the spectacular moonlike crater in the central Negev, where mining moltmorillonite could make jobs for the tiny mining community of Mizpe Ramon, which hangs on the lip of the crater.

The work Bunin is doing with the microscopic particles will ultimately help maintain the citrus plantations, avocado trees, and other crops sensitive to soil-aeration problems, and talking to him, one gets the feeling he is a dirt farmer at heart, even though his education and expertise are scientific. Such a phenomenon is not unusual in Israel, where Itzhak Alpan, at the Technion, the earthquake expert (who would love to have more time and attention paid to earthquake engineering and seismology) uses his great knowledge of soil mechanics to help solve building and construction problems, and plant geneticist David Vofsi at the Weizmann Institute ties his work on cucumbers and tomatoes to the problems of mechanical harvesting.

Mineral studies of other parts of Israel, beyond the Dead Sea and the Negev, have failed to turn up much in the way of potential resources for major exploitation, with the exception of the copper mined in King Solomon's mines at Timna, which is mixed with scrap iron and other ingredients for export as copper cement. But even this is not a mineral resource in any way comparable to that of the Dead Sea.

Glass-manufacturing, using local resources, is expanding. A traditional industry going back into antiquity, glass-making at the Phoenicia Glass Works in Haifa just recently expanded to include the manufacture of high quality plate glass. All ingredients but the soda ash, which must be imported, can be found in Israel.

Israel is not rich in oil resources but is on the verge of becoming a major oil-exporting nation. In the 1950's, Leo Picard picked up the threads of oil exploration carried on by the Turks, the Germans, the British, and various oil companies before the State of Israel was formed and helped find the Heletz oil fields at Ashkelon, one of Palestine's most ancient cities. Although these oil fields have never provided more than 8 per cent of the oil used by the country—to operate power plants, in industrial production of polyethylene, which is widely used in agriculture and elsewhere, for lubrication, and other purposes—the development of the Heletz wells and the building of pipelines from the oil port at Eilat have led to the construction of new refineries in the Ashkelon area and the creation of major oil port facilities in the Ashkelon-Ashdod harbor complexes.

What set Israel up as a major oil-exporting nation was the completion of the third and largest pipeline from Eilat in February, 1970. This 42-inch pipeline, which runs over rough terrain 165 miles through the Negev, is the successor to the original Eilat-Beersheba pipeline built after the Sinai campaign. Within a year's time, additional pumping capability now being constructed will give the new pipeline a total capacity of 60 million tons a year, more than one-third the capacity of the Suez Canal in 1966. Port facilities adequate to handle the new 150,000-ton tankers, and larger, will make it possible for the Israeli tanker fleet and other large ships to carry Israeli-refined oil and crude oil to European and other markets through the Mediterranean. Some of the oil will come from the Heletz fields and some from the occupied Sinai Desert, but most of it will be offloaded in Eilat and piped over the Negev mountains and gullies to Ashkelon. It will make Israel economically self-sufficient insofar as oil is concerned, with import costs balanced by import incomes.

(The building of the pipeline, incidentally, was another triumph of Israeli engineering, and, true to the Israeli fashion, an imported pipe-bending machine was nicknamed the "bagel-maker." The project was directed by two Technion graduates.)

As a result of the oil discoveries and other developments, chemical industry complexes are expanding at Arad, Oron, Haifa, and Ashkelon. At the Jerusalem economic conference in 1969, a survey of the chemical industry—including those firms making pharmaceuticals, veterinary medicines, and other products under license from foreign countries—showed that the investment in fixed assets tripled between 1967 and 1968.

But by far the largest in terms of size and potential volume of export output are those industries that are based on utilization of Israel's own resources—the Dead Sea phosphates and other Negev minerals such as moltmorillonite, the Heletz oilfield and the oil pipelines, and the Timna copper mines. The early dreams of Novemeysky and Picard, crystallized by hard research at the Hebrew University, the Technion, the Weizmann Institute, and government research laboratories, have provided Israel with an economic and industrial future that utilizes to the fullest the nation's scanty but unique mineral resources. Much of this will continue to come from a stagnant body of water and a desert that had gone relatively untouched and unappreciated for thousands of years, along whose shores the roads opened to get to the minerals are now also beginning to serve tourists and farmers.

VIII

Human Health Problems

When the new State of Israel opened its doors to all Jewish immigrants, striking out the health and age bars that the British Mandate Government had established, it also opened the door to immediate and potential health problems.

These problems included the possibility of new outbreaks of such previously eradicated diseases as malaria and bilharzia, enteric ailments resulting from primitive sanitation, eye and skin infections common to the Middle East, and a high rate of infant mortality. There was also the immediate need for expanded health and medical services for a rapidly growing population and the problem of climatic adaptation on the part of immigrants from temperate climates.

Most of these problems were not new, of course, for the history of Jewish settlement in Palestine is a running story of battles against malarial infestation, debilitating disease, the effects of desert heat, and struggles to raise health standards. Fortunately for the new immigrants, Israel had a strong foundation of medical service and research to build on, as well as a larger-than-average supply of doctors and scientists, many of whom had fled the Nazis in Europe just before the outbreak of World War II.

In spite of the phenomenal population growth, Israel has one of the highest ratios of doctors per population—one for every 426 persons—of any country in the world, and the medical research being carried on at the Hebrew University–Hadassah Medical School, the Weizmann Institute, the University of Tel Aviv, the Tel Hashomer military hospital, and various government hospitals is linked to the world's leading research institutions. Until the recent clampdown of U.S. Government funds, for example, Israeli scientists did more health research for the U.S. Government than was being done by medical researchers in any other country.

The story of Israeli medical and health science begins in the early years of the twentieth century. Until after World War I, when the British initiated some antismallpox and malaria programs and created rudimentary public health services, health conditions in Palestine can only be described as atrocious, although the Jews had already begun to develop their own health services.

In 1912, the Histadrut labor federation founded Kupat Holim, a comprehensive health insurance program, which brought care to the cooperative villages and collective settlements. Today, Kupat Holim covers seven out of every ten Israelis. A year later, Hadassah sent two nurses from the United States to provide maternal- and child-health services for Jewish, Moslem, and Christian mothers in old Jerusalem. In 1918, the American Zionist Medical Unit, jointly sponsored by Hadassah and the Joint Distribution Committee, sent forty-four doctors, nurses, sanitary engineers, and other personnel to establish hospitals in Tiberias, Safed, Jaffa, Haifa, and Jerusalem. They opened the school of nursing in Jerusalem, played a part in the creation of the Hebrew University Medical School a few years later, and gave Palestine its first organized system of mother-and-baby-care stations and school health- and luncheon-programs.

Prior to 1948, the draining of the swamps and the combined efforts of the British Government and the Jewish organizations brought about vast public health improvements. During this same period, few sick or elderly immigrants were allowed into Palestine, and, by 1947, malaria had been almost eradicated, all children were vaccinated against smallpox and typhoid, and infant and adult mortality rates were low.

The New State of Israel established a Ministry of Health to supervise health activities and provide public health and preventive medical services. The new Ministry had scarcely come into existence when the great waves of immigrants brought with them the problems of sickness and aging.

Many world health authorities gloomily predicted that this wide-open immigration policy would bring all sorts of epidemics, especially with so many people carrying endemic diseases from the Arab and other underdeveloped countries. One group of 45,000 Yemenite Jews, who trekked across the desert in 1949 to Aden and were thence flown to Israel, included 20,000 bilharzia-carriers, 27,000 cases of trachoma and 8,000 of tropical ulcer, 20,000 people with malaria, and many with tuberculosis. Many were hospitalized immediately upon arrival,. while those with active bilharzia posed a danger that the water-borne debilitating disease would spread through the country's many irrigation lakes and fish-ponds. Another group, from India, arrived in 1954 and 1955, bringing not only trachoma, tuberculosis, ringworm, and intestinal worms, but also filariasis. Although this particular disease (often called elephantiasis) was new to Israel, the mosquitoes that carry it were not. Other immigrants from Algeria and Tunisia brought in more ringworm, malaria, and tuberculosis, and included many who were blind, crippled, or mentally retarded. In addition, there were Eastern European immigrants with lung or other ailments resulting from the hardships they had experienced during and after World War II.

It was six years before Israeli public health authorities finally mastered the massive job that faced them and were able to institute pre-immigration health examinations that permitted separation of the ill for treatment upon arrival. By 1967, the Ministry of Health, Hadassah, Kupat Holim, Malben (a branch of the Joint Distribution Committee), and other groups were operating 658 maternal- and child-health stations and 142 hospitals throughout the country, with psychiatric and rehabilitation facilities as well as institutions for the mentally retarded.

Health facilities have been provided for both Jewish and Arab communities. And, since the Six-Day War, a team of Israeli doctors and nurses has brought vast improvements to the old Egyptian hospital at El Arish in the occupied Sinai peninsula. Kupat Holim has over a thousand clinics and nine general hospitals among its services, which also include nursing homes, pharmacies, and a research institute. Hadassah operates the big hospital adjoining the Hebrew University Medical School at Ein Kerem and other facilities. The government has many hospitals and clinics. The Mogen David Adom, Israel's equivalent of the Red Cross, provides a blood donor program that is equipped to provide both whole blood and blood components on a quickly expandable scale, as during the Six-Day War, and a nationwide first-aid- and ambulance-service. By virtue of the fact that, during the War of Independence, the Sinai campaign, and the Six-Day War, donors in other countries provided the Mogen David Adom with blood fractionation equipment, that organization was able to produce all of the blood components and fractions needed throughout the Middle East. The organization also produces snakebite serums.

It is well-nigh impossible to list all of the advances made by Israeli medicine and research. A summary of research projects published by the Hebrew University early in 1970 lists 880 for the Faculty of Medicine, sixty-seven in the School of Pharmacy, and sixty-one in the Faculty of Dental Medicine. At the Weizmann Institute, there are scores of research projects related to cancer, human molecular structure, viruses, and other fields being carried out by biologists, geneticists, chemists, radiologists, and other scientists. By virtue of the gathering of people from so many places, Israel has become a focal point for a great variety of research. There is intense research on trachoma and rheumatic fever and a continuing effort to prevent malaria from again becoming a problem. Most of the standard inoculations or vaccinations were introduced in the 1950's. When the Salk vaccine against polio came into general use in 1955, Israel manufactured its own because enough could not be purchased on the open market. Vaccination against tuberculosis has been standard since 1951.

The tradition of medical research goes back to the first laboratory set up by Dr. Saul Adler, who became world famous while heading the Hebrew University's Department of Parasitology.

Adler is loath to talk about his achievements, but he has earned, among other awards, the Chalmers Medal of the Royal Society of Tropical Medicine and Hygiene for his work on leishmaniasis, one form of which is "Oriental Sore," which he discovered was transmitted by the ubiquitous sandflies. His department was recognized by the World Health Organization of the United Nations as the international Reference Library in this field. He and his colleagues are known also for their work in human and animal parasitic diseases, having found that the local cave tick transmitted relapsing fever, developed vaccinations against dreaded theileriasis, which could have wiped out the Palestinian dairy industry, and done work with malaria parasites and on leprosy in hamsters. One unusual contribution to the world of scientific research—use of the hamster—originated with Adler. At his request, naturalist Israel Aharoni brought to Adler's laboratory a family of three golden hamsters. They were bred for the first time as research animals at the Hebrew University, and are now used worldwide.

"I took the first opportunity of distributing them to various laboratories," Adler recalls. "I brought animals to the College de France, to the Wellcome Bureau of Scientific Research, and to the Medical Research Council in London. Later I sent batches of them to India and to Egypt. All the golden hamsters in all the laboratories and pet shops of the world are descended from the original three brought to our department."

After being formally constituted as the Department of Parasitology in 1938, Adler's group moved to larger quarters on Mount Scopus, where, in addition to its regular work, it worked on malaria and dysentery for the Allied armies in World War II. In 1948, when Mount Scopus was cut off, the Department of Parasitology moved into the center of Jerusalem. It is now at the new Medical School at Ein Kerem. In spite of its important work, it has always struggled with low budgets—not until 1962 could Adler afford a secretary. When he retired in 1965, his only comment on his achievements was a modest, "I don't think I've done the University any harm." Still far from satisfied, he added, "There is an enormous amount of work yet to be done, particularly in the field of animal diseases. Tick-borne animal diseases, for example, still constitute a major problem in this country, and facilities for their study must be provided. There should also be a laboratory for the study of pathogens and infected tissues."

The work goes on. Although malaria is no longer an important problem in Israel, there is always the possibility that new drug-resistant forms of the disease will appear—as they have among U.S. troops in Vietnam—or that the disease will spread back to Israel from surrounding countries or be brought in by immigrants from the many parts of the world where it remains endemic. As a contribution to other areas where malaria control would be phenomenally expensive—as in Equatorial Africa and the Far East—the department continues its work under the direction of Professor Avivah Zuckerman, who became interested in the subject while studying for her Ph.D. at the University of Chicago. As part of the American war effort, she joined a malarial research program sponsored by the U.S. Office of Scientific Research and Development. Ultimately, she wrote her doctoral thesis on malaria immunology and has been working in the field ever since. Her researches have taken her to many parts of the world and are financed not only by the University but by the World Health Organization, the National Institutes of Health in the United States, and the U.S. Army. One breakthrough, by Dr. Dan Spira of the Department of Parasitology, is a method of separating the malaria parasite from the red blood cell in which it is embedded. Other studies, aimed at isolating one particular protective antibody, could lead to the creation of an antimalarial vaccine, which would be a major triumph.

One of the most recent Israeli medical successes has been the demonstration by Hebrew University–Hadassah Medical School virologists that the drug, rifampicin, can be used to treat trachoma, an eye disease endemic to the Middle East. Some years ago, the late Professor Hans Bernkopf discovered that the disease was carried by a viruslike bacterium. Experiments led to rifampicin as an antibiotic to control this particular agent. Another series of studies by Dr. Isaac Ginsburg, a microbiologist and immunologist, shows promise of uncovering the role of white cells in the blood stream, which, in addition to their disease-fighting functions, may also be involved in carrying streptococci and other bacteria to various parts of the body where they cause everything from gum diseases to arthritis and polio.

The Hebrew University has also been involved in a massive study of rheumatic fever. This study was initially begun in Jerusalem, where there was a high incidence of the disease among children. Researchers have found strong evidence that heredity rather than conditions of poverty may be the more important factor in the disease's prevalance, although it is usually more severe among the poor. A statistical analysis of more than 2,000 families in which the disease occurred—families of diverse origins who represented all economic levels—has led to the notion that heredity may be the guiding factor involved in the ailment's occurrence.

Other research, done in cooperation with researchers in other countries, led to the discovery that one amino acid present in corneal cells can preserve the water-pumping efficiency of these cells and thus preserve their transparency, a discovery of great importance to eye banks. And, at the Weizmann Institute, work of considerable importance is being done on the molecular transfer of cancer cells.

The recent award of the 1970 Albert Schweitzer memorial prize to a young Israeli doctor, Mordecai Shani, recognizes the fact that the Israelis also do considerable public health work among the Arabs. Dr. Shani, of the staff of Tel Hashomer Hospital, headed the team that went down to El Arish in the Sinai after the Six-Day War to revitalize the hospitals and clinics that were left a shambles by the retreating Egyptians. Together with other volunteer doctors and Israeli nurses who had been born in Arab countries and spoke Arabic, they turned the underequipped hospitals and clinics in Gaza and outlying areas into models of public health service.

Israeli medical schools teach students from almost a score of developing countries, and Hebrew University and Mogen David Adom teams have traveled far and wide in Africa to help develop public-health and first-aid training programs.

Over and beyond medical research per se, Israel has done a great deal of what might be called "human engineering" in a continuing effort to help the immigrant adapt to the environment. The Technion has a "Human Engineering" unit, which provides an integrated, interdisciplinary approach to a vast variety of problems such as human response to high temperatures, the designing of artificial limbs for the war wounded, and air and noise pollution.

Examples of Technion's human engineering include the creation of a light-weight, gas-operated arm developed by Dr. Dino Buosso of the Technion while doing research at Oxford's Department of Engineering. Lighter, more maneuverable, and controlled by the wearer's brain impulses, this new artificial limb was designed for thalidomide victims. Buosso had previously worked closely with the military to develop prosthetic devices for battle-wounded soldiers.

Technion, Hebrew University, and Negev Institute scientists have done a great deal of work on the problem of acclimatization, some in experimental housing construction described in the next chapter, but a great deal of it focusing directly on immediate human reactions.

Shlomo Samueloff, a round-faced Sofia-born physiologist, is probably best known because he was one of the two Israeli men held in prison in Syria after Arab terrorists hijacked a TWA airliner, but, long before that incident, he had earned a name among specialists for his research on climatic adaptation, which he became interested in in 1956. The first studies, in Beersheba, sought to determine the seasonal and diurnal variations in the human body's acid content. Researchers followed fourteen people for a year, taking blood samples every two or three weeks at different times of the day. Although the project had considerable support from the local army commander at Beersheba, the project got off to many false starts because the military participants had other duties and their participation was irregular. So the researchers turned to the general population, starting with townspeople who were living in desert conditions (there was no air conditioning in those days). At the peak of the summer heat, they also studied a group of potash-workers from Sdom, where it was even hotter. The study found seasonal variations in the blood-acid levels of the subjects, with a slight tendency toward increased acidification in the blood stream during the summer, especially among the Dead Sea group. The changes were seen as a strictly biological problem, and it was concluded that, if an individual was physically fit, there would be no pathological changes because of the intense climate. For another year, the studies continued, this time concentrating on energy expenditures at different levels of work. Again, it was concluded that the energy expenditures were constant and that the failure to develop significant statistical patterns was the result of the varying climate. Further studies, growing in complexity, compared tall Kurds from the mountains with smaller Yemenites. (The Yemenites, it turned out, drank little water but ate lots of cucumbers; some of the researchers got sick from eating so many cucumbers during the study.) Multidisciplinary studies involving both psychology and physiology included such factors as water intake, work habits, absenteeism, and productivity and went far beyond the original strictly physiological testing until it was finally concluded that climatic adaptation was not the problem it had been feared. The Israeli researchers decided that any man in good health who was motivated to do so, could adapt to the desert climate and overheated working conditions in a few weeks.

These studies by Samueloff and others did provide good insights into problems of working- and living-conditions and prompted another physiologist, Israeli-born Esar Shvartz, a graduate of the University of Southern California, to undertake the design of body-cooling helmets for Dead Sea workers. His earlier research, conducted in controlled climate chambers, showed that cooling the head and neck would be sufficient to increase the comfort of men working on laboratory treadmills in temperatures of more than 100°F. Shvartz's research is related to the problem of lower productivity on the part of men working at the Dead Sea or in factories in the area around the Negev Institute, where he is located. A physical education specialist as well as a physiologist (and the after-hours author of a book on existentialism and sports), Shvartz believes that heat acclimatization can be achieved in four to five days if necessary but that a better plan is to put an individual in a hot room for just one hour a day for two weeks. Plain physical exercise does the same thing, for the body temperature goes up with running and similar activities. (The Germans used this kind of regimen on soldiers being transferred from the eastern front to Africa during World War II.)

Technion researchers, sponsored by the U.S. Public Health Service and the Histadrut labor federation, are working to determine the relationship between sunlight exposure and physiological heat strain under different working conditions and with different kinds of clothing. They hope to develop a small transistorized sensing unit to keep track of workers' pulse rates. The pulse rate reflects the balance between the body's internal heat load and the cooling efficiency of sweating. The miniradios would transmit the pulse rates to a central monitor where a supervisor could order rest periods for workers whose pulse rates neared the danger point.

Several interesting Technion projects involve noise and its effects on people in an industrializing nation. One in particular is related to the growing Israel traffic problem—a real hazard, as anyone who has dodged an Egged bus can testify. This project is studying the effect of sustained noise on the fatigue, vision, and reaction time of bus drivers. Another study, important in a multilingual nation such as Israel, is investigating the effect of static and external hums on English, Hebrew, French, and German transmitted by radio or telephone.

One study of climatic effect had an unexpected result—the suggestion that Israelis leave their country periodically. This was research done by Professor Felix Gad Sulman, head of the Department of Applied Pharmacology at the Hebrew University, who spent four years investigating the metabolic effect on people in Israel of the *hamseen*—a period of extreme dry heat that arrives on an easterly wind from the Arabian deserts and sweeps over Israel, sending the temperature soaring while reducing the humidity to 25 per cent or less. One Israeli writer says that "These are the days—and in Jerusalem there can be as many as 150 of them in one year—when the veteran population goes to pieces. The longer they have been living in the country, the more they suffer."

Tourists don't seem at all bothered by *hamseens*. But healthy Israelis become tense and lose their alertness. Low-blood-pressure sufferers feel it even more, and the allergic get migraines, hay fever, and asthma. Sulman, having watched people suffer for a long time—he arrived in Israel in 1934—finally sought a grant from Hadassah to study the changes that occur in human metabolism when a *hamseen* strikes Jerusalem. He found, for example, that perspiration doubles, the loss of salts through sweating quintuples, and the blood is flooded with potassium. Worst of all, there is a cumulative effect on the adrenal glands, so that the body adjusts to the desert weather phenomenon less and less.

Apparently tourists and new immigrants produce enough adrenalin to counter the effects of the *hamseen* on their bodies, while the old-timers and the *sabras* can't. Sulman is now investigating possible counterdrugs or whether drinking a lot of strong coffee might help make living easier at *hamseen* time. At this point, about all he can recommend is a sort of short-term emigration, with Israelis going abroad to cooler climates to store up fresh adrenalin-making capacity in their bodies.

Industrial environment, too, is a problem in Israel as elsewhere. The Hebrew University–Hadassah Medical School Laboratory of Occupational Health, headed by Rumanian Professor Marcus Wasserman, has a small staff but a big job. Their main research area is evaluating the toxic hazards from the manufacture and use of pesticides. By pointing to the DDT problem, for example, they were able to institute precautions against misuse of the insecticide, with the result that the level of DDT in the bodies of the farmers under observation dropped markedly in just two years. The laboratory has also found that the high temperatures of the Israeli summer increase the rate at which a farmer's body absorbs insecticides—a serious problem for a country where so much intensified agriculture is carried on in high temperatures. Wasserman's staff is also helping to alleviate the dust threat to Timna copper-miners and cement-factory workers.

Not all acclimatization in Israel is heat related. Eating habits have been a health problem, especially with large numbers of immigrants from North Africa, who do not normally eat the kind of food available in their new homeland. Among the problems involving the eating habits of North African Jews was their dependence on white bread and rice. To this group, white bread was a status symbol; they were not interested in more nutritious whole wheat varieties. Food-producers had to enrich white bread to be certain the North African immigrants got proper nourishment. Also, the Yemenites and other North Africans were used to a rice diet. Rice is not raised in Israel. To help them adjust to other grains, the Ministry of Agriculture had the Esom food manufacturing company make rice-sized pasta out of wheat and other grains, so that Yemenite cooking habits could be continued with an acceptable rice substitute.

The end result of Israeli medical, physiological, and industrial health research is that the continuing rapid population growth has not run into the great problems of epidemics and heat exhaustion predicted by the doubting Thomases—another important victory for the technology of necessity.

IX

To House a Nation

In the summer of 1969, Sascha Koussewitzky, who has been a camel-driver, surveyor working on Negev pipeline projects, potash-trucker, tax-assessor, Haganah and Israeli Army machine gunner, among other things, began a new career assessing properties or areas slated for urban redevelopment in Jerusalem. The tanned, wiry Israeli, who, in the 1930's, helped build the prefabricated instant tower-and-stockade border settlements, now works in areas where he is surrounded by multistoried blocks of modern apartments, fast-rising additional construction, and overcrowded crumbling relics that have housed thousands of newcomers to Palestine. In his lifetime, he has seen a sparsely settled land become a bustling nation of almost 3 million people, with tens of thousands more arriving every year. The urban renewal projects on which he is now working are part of a proposal to double Jerusalem's present Jewish population of 200,000 in the next four to thirteen years.

Koussewitzky himself lives in a cool, high-ceilinged flat in a lovely old home surrounded by gardens in the Rehavia section of Jerusalem, within walking distance of the busy, bustling downtown section, where a high-rise apartment house towers over a large supermarket and a growing area of new blocks of housing. His son, Israeli-born Donny, a veteran of the Israel Air Force and now controller in the tower at the Jerusalem airport, lives with his two children and his wife in a crowded apartment development on the opposite side of the city. From his windows, he can see similar developments and water towers topping the ridges of the nearby Judean Hills and in the distance the magnificently modern Hadassah Hospital complex overlooking Ein Kerem. The father lives in surroundings reflecting the old garden-style development of the pre-State architects who brought with them to Palestine the legacy of European approaches to community planning and building. The son lives in housing that reflects the new State of Israel's intensive effort to house its growing population.

Far to the north and south of the Koussewitzky's two homes, still another kind of housing and community development was going up in the summer of 1969. It, too, reflects the urgent needs of the nation—this time to defend its borders.

In the occupied Golan Heights, from which Syrian gunners once harassed Israeli farmers on the slopes below, new agricultural settlements, new *kibbutzim* and *moshavem,* are being established by young soldiers who alternate between defending the border and turning the rocky, relatively unused soil into productive farmland. At El-Al, in the southern part of the Heights, for example, a new *moshav* in mid-1969 already had three married couples and four children. Many additional people wanted to join the group but could not for lack of housing. Nor is housing the only problem. Old water pipes lose two of every three gallons of water as it is carried fifteen miles from its source to El-Al. In spite of these and other difficulties, all of the original members of the first group of settlers are still there, and have managed to cultivate more than 1,600 acres and raise hundreds of sheep and thousands of geese.

Young settlers of Nahal Tsofar—one of Israel's unique military farm settlements, which are usually the first to spring up along the borders or in new territories—during the same summer of 1969, watched a bulldozer clear the ground for the first small white stone houses that would replace the tents in which they had been living. Their new home is in the Arava, along the lonely, barren stretch of border. It was established in September, 1968, on the site of an agronomical research station. The forty-second such army pioneer settlement created by the Israelis,

Nahal Tsofar is intended to help close the fifty-six-mile gap between 'En Yahav and Gerofit on the Israel-Jordan border and to use the land and water resources of that part of the Arava for winter cultivation. Nahal Tsofar's first night as a tent settlement was marked by rocket attacks from Arab guerrilla bases in the Edom Mountains across the valley. They destroyed the vital water-pumping machinery. But, less than a year later, the nation's housing industry was bringing permanent structures to the locale. By late 1970, the settlement was to be transformed into a civilian *kibbutz*, with regular housing, grass lawns, and all the accoutrements of a new farm community.

Although urban planning and rural development are not exactly science and technology in the purest sense, Israeli experience in this field has involved not only the sheer brute strength of a building industry and its labor force but also the technical expertise of architects, geologists, engineers, research scientists, and even meteorologists. The results may not have been all that might be desired, but the new State managed to treble its population without forcing a single immigrant to sleep under the stars for even one night.

Israel has a legacy of planned community design that goes back into the 1920's, when architect Richard Kauffmann created the first truly planned villages of modern times, and has converted that legacy into the building of planned new cities and towns that long predate the advent of "new communities" such as Columbia and Reston near the U.S. capital and similar experiments in Europe. Unfortunately, Israel has also a legacy of having to rely on massive temporary housing programs and of permitting haphazard overcrowding of its larger cities. Thus, a nation less than a quarter of a century old is already dealing with the problems of slum clearance—especially in the large cities of Jerusalem, Tel Aviv, and Haifa, and smaller but older communities such as Petah Tikvah.

Although Jewish Palestine was founded on the basis of agricultural settlement, less than 18 per cent of Israel's population today is rural; two-thirds of the population lives in cities and towns and another 17 per cent in the suburbs around them. The famed *kibbutzim*, which have come to symbolize Zionist development in Palestine, account for less than 85,000 people, or only about 3 per cent of the total population, and the total proportion of agricultural population will continue shrinking as the nation industrializes and farming becomes more mechanized.

Nonetheless, Kauffmann, who planned the early agricultural settlements to take advantage of terrain, prevailing winds and the needs of the settlers, and who also planned some of the new sections of larger cities such as Tel Aviv and Haifa, would probably, if he were alive today, look with approval at the creation of such "instant cities" as Kiryat Shmona in the far north, Dimona and Oron in the Negev, and Ashdod, Israel's newest major seaport, for these towns were developed as total planning packages to include homes, industries, essential services and schools, and the other ingredients of a full-blown community. And, even though many of the pioneer settlements were established before he arrived on the scene, any story of housing development in Israel has to start with Kauffmann. He was born in Frankfurt-am-Main in 1877, and he studied architecture and town planning in an era when the field was in its infancy. One of his earliest projects, before World War I, was planning of workers' settlements for the Krupp plant at Essen. As his career developed, he was brought to Palestine by Arthur Ruppin of the Zionist Commission to direct town planning projects. An Israeli newspaper tribute to Kauffmann's work published in 1959, a year after his death read in part:

> Kauffmann was called here by Ruppin to direct the town planning projects which were to be an integral part of Jewish settlement of this country. At the time, this connection was far from a matter of course, and the solitary planner was deprived of the facilities he needed to establish it, as well as of the understanding of his colleagues. Yet he understood the challenge and proved equal to it. For the first time, villages and agricultural settlements were systematically planned by an architect—an epoch-making step that has only recently been imitated in other countries. In his plans, Kauffmann combined the necessary technical and security aspects with the main intention, namely, the mould for a new kind of communal living.
>
> He developed basic designs for the smallholders' village, the *kibbutz*, and the cooperative settlement. In a typical *kibbutz*

design, he would take advantage of the climate by opening the houses to the northwest to provide access for prevailing breezes. Farm buildings were on the east, so the wind would not blow from them toward the houses. Living quarters and work buildings were separated by green strips, and traffic was routed so it would interfere minimally with the residential areas.

He invariably took advantage of existing hillocks and topography to put main community centers and communal quarters on a rise as near the center of the farming areas as possible. Recognizing the drawbacks of design rigidity, he always utilized differing terrains to vary the specific layouts. He was the first architect in Israel to tackle directly the problem of the climate, with its extremely hot summers and its heavy but short-lived winter rainfalls, which ordinarily would imply the use of expensive insulating materials, especially for roofs, and heavy asphalt shingling against the rains. Kauffmann found other, less costly, solutions. For one school at Deganya, in the hot, below-sea-level Jordan Valley, he mounted a Ternolit roof on a wooden framework two yards above the ceiling so that winds could circulate between the two roofs and cool the classrooms. So impressed by this was the manager of the potash works at the even hotter Dead Sea that he asked Kauffmann to build similar structures at the works there. Kauffmann came up with elaborate plans for the development of both Haifa and Tel Aviv, but they were not carried out. One plan that was completed was the development of the garden suburb of Beit Hakerem, which harmonizes with the natural rock terraces outside Jerusalem. He also designed many of the cool, lovely homes in the Rehavia section of Jerusalem.

History, however, was not on Kauffmann's side. From 1939 on, virtually no building had taken place in Palestine, so that, when the flood of immigration began with the creation of the new State in mid-1948, there was no alternative except to build and build and build. Even the thousands of small houses abandoned by Arab families who chose to leave the country could only offer housing to less than a third of the immigrants who had arrived by the end of 1951.

Between 1948 and 1967, some 775,000 housing units were required, about 45 per cent of them for new immigrants. During this same period, 585,000 permanent units were built, 65,000 of them temporary Nissen huts, or asbestos or wooden huts. Of the new buildings constructed by the government, almost three-quarters were for immigrants, with the result that many of the older residents and newly married young couples were forced to continue in overcrowded homes or even to live on in slum areas. Obviously, then, there is still a great need for more new housing and for slum clearance and urban renewal, especially since many of today's newer immigrants—middle-class professional people, for the most part—are demanding and being given even larger housing accommodations than their predecessors. (Whereas early immigrants were given living quarters of 376 to 484 square feet, many of the new flats run to as much as 916 square feet.

In the years immediately following the establishment of the State, even the permanent building program had to give way to temporary metal huts and other expedients to provide winter housing for the new arrivals. Immigrant camps, called *ma'abara,* were hastily erected, some combining tents and metal huts, some made of asbestos or prefabricated, imported wooden walls. By 1950, there were almost 100,000 people living in fifty-three such camps. When it became apparent that the people were settling in, and wanted to remain right where they were, plans had to be made to construct permanent communities in the same locales, but it was not until the late 1960's that the last *ma'abara* was closed down.

Meanwhile, Israel had decided not only how to build houses but also where to put them. One observer wrote that:

> ... the country was like a pressure cooker, bubbling and boiling with new arrivals; a man was sent to live not where the job was, but where the apartment was. Reasons are simple. The house was put on the map before the job . . Thus, if one were offered a house in a farming settlement, that, as often as not, was enough to make him turn farmer.

Gradually, the government was able to evolve a national plan for population dispersal. When the State was formed, half the

people of Israel lived in or around Tel Aviv, Haifa, and Jerusalem. By the mid-1960's, only 31 per cent of the population
lived in these areas. In this time, Beersheba—a lonely outpost
and caravan stop—grew to a city of close to 70,000, Eilat from a
handful of shacks to 11,000, Herzliya to 35,000, Bat Yam to
62,000, and new cities such as Ashdod and Dimona acquired
sizable populations.

In most countries, new communities have been created to re-
lieve the burden on overcrowded metropolitan areas, but Israel
faced a historical necessity for changing the population from one
of a densely populated coastal area and sparsely settled northern,
southern, and inland areas to a spread that would create both
political and military security. When the new government in
1948 faced a need for a whole new system of towns, more than
three-fourths of the population was concentrated in 11.1 per cent
of the country. Jews and non-Jews together came to 7.6 settlers
per square mile in the south as compared to 5,000 per square
mile in Tel Aviv. Soon after the formation of the State, a National
Planning Council was created, and this has guided the development of the country ever since. The largest part of the new housing has been built by the government, which also provides the
roads, water, power, and necessary services for all new communities.

Kiryat Gat, Dimona, Oron, Kiryat Shmona, and Ashdod are
good examples of new development towns.

Kiryat Gat, near the site where Goliath was born, was built
in the southern cotton-growing area after the introduction of
cotton in the 1950's. It has cotton gins and plants for textile-
spinning, dyeing, and finishing, as well as a sugar factory to
process the new sugarbeet crops now grown on farms in the area.
It is located on the railroad and is the focal point for the growing
agricultural Lakhish area south of Tel Aviv and near the oil city
of Ashkelon. The city was built on flat land with few topographical problems and prevailing winds that eased the potential climatological difficulties. The first master plan called for a population of 14,000; it has been raised to about 80,000. The center of
town is a small piazza with administrative offices, a community
hall, stores, restaurants, movie theaters, and the usual public-

building complex. The industrial zone to the east is close to the railroad. The residential areas have been described as a housing history of recent Israeli town planning. The first quarter, to the east, consists of typical, old-style, one-story, one- and two-family homes with large garden plots. The second quarter, to the southwest, has mostly single-story garden homes, although here there are also the first of the terrace apartments. Plots are smaller than in the first quarter. A few three-story blocks of flats have been built on the edges of the quarter, whereas the third quarter to the northwest is largely two- and three-story blocks. A new model neighborhood, incorporating the newest designs aimed at meeting both climatic conditions and the needs of later immigrants, will have the highest population density—eighteen units per acre as compared to two dwellings per acre in the first section built.

Kiryat Shmona near the Lebanese border (it is subject to repeated rocketings by guerrillas operating from Lebanon) was created to provide a population center in the remote northern border areas and has its own commercial and industrial complex. The town is on the northwestern rim of the Hula basin, three hours by bus from Haifa, and in a mountainous region that is hot in the summer and cold and rainy in the winter. The area was densely settled until the fourteenth century when the people left and it reverted to malarial swampland. It was not even sparsely resettled until 500 years later, when groups of freed slaves, military deserters, and other outcasts founded some small, unsuccessful villages. The first Jewish settlements in the 1880's were decimated by malaria, and, only much later, was any successful settlement begun. Today the region has almost forty agricultural settlements and the city of Kiryat Shmona, started in 1950, adjacent to the tents, huts, and barracks of an immigrant camp. Literally translated, Kiryat Shmona means "Town of the Eight." It is named after a group of settlers who lost their lives in the Arab raids of 1920.

Although the country around Kiryat Shmona is lush, the town's site is far from promising. It is squeezed in between the mountains, occupying space in the valley and on the slopes. The area east of the main road, which bisects the elongated town, was reserved for small holdings and one- and two-family homes, while the rising ground on the slopes to the west is covered by two- and three-story terrace houses and blocks of flats. The town center, with its shops, movie theater, public buildings, and other facilities, is west of the main road, and the industrial section is in the valley. Eventually its population may reach 30,000, for there is plenty of room for expansion, although there is a lack of both agricultural and industrial employment, especially for teenagers leaving vocational schools.

Dimona was built initially to house laborers from the Dead Sea Works who had been living in climatic misery, separated from their families for weeks on end. Construction of the so-called impossible road to Sdom made it practical to provide a livable "home community" for the men who toiled in the great heat and humidity at the big chemical plants far below sea level. (Somewhat similarly, the town of Oron was established to provide housing for workers employed in the exploitation of Negev phosphate deposits.)

The new harbor city of Ashdod was built from scratch because Israel needed a southern port on the Mediterranean. It represents one of the nation's largest projects. Originally designed for 150,000 residents, Ashdod now looks forward to a population of 350,000. Its port will handle more than 4 million tons of cargo annually, more than goes through Haifa, and the big new 150,000-ton tankers are loading there, now that the 42-inch pipeline from Eilat to the nearby Ashkelon refineries and oil fields has been completed. The port is an outlet, also, for chemicals and potash from the Dead Sea and the Negev as well as agricultural and other products from southern farms and industry. A large power plant has already been built, and the city will be the site of the world's largest desalination project when and if that effort is finally financed. Ashdod has sixteen projected residential areas connected by a network of roads and streets, each with its own shopping and community center. Because the population is, for the most part, new immigrants and working class, most of the housing is large blocks of flats rather than single or two-family units.

Another newly developed seaport, Eilat, on the Gulf of Aqaba at the southern tip of pre-1967 Israel, also has large blocks of flats, many of them made with prefabricated materials trucked in or brought in by ship to house the port workers and miners from the nearby Timna copper diggings. Eilat is also the site of many large new beachfront hotels that make it resemble a skimpy Miami Beach. Only recently an inaccessible, small port so difficult to live in because of the heat and remoteness that its residents were given tax-exempt status, Eilat has become a major seaport and an important resort area, notwithstanding the fact that it is under the guns of Jordan (the Jordanian port of Aqaba is across the bay from Eilat) and ships are subject to attack by Arab frogmen.

A major achievement has been the expansion of Beersheba, the so-called capital of the Negev, from a tiny town in which early residents carried water from wells and read by oil lamps to a thriving community of perhaps 80,000 residents. This city's designers received the R. S. Reynolds Award for Community Architecture for 1969 as an "outstanding symbol of the Israeli new urbanization programme." The judges, of the American Institute of Architects, selected Beersheba's design because "it represents the full spectrum for community evolution. It is, in the totality of development of new and old, an outstanding symbol of a national urbanization policy." They found the Beersheba plan, which blends environment with structure in the center buildings by using open-air galleries and provides a variety of high-rise apartments, offers different living styles in keeping with the natural surroundings. Existing buildings have been blended into the new design; for example, expansion of the old town center with the addition of a central market retained the Oriental characteristics of the older buildings. Industries have been confined to the outskirts of the city.

A typical rural development now nearing completion, involves stepping up the population of western Galilee with thirty-five farm villages built around rural centers and already existing towns. The Israelis have also been developing special housing units for the Bedouins, at Ramle and Beersheba, to bring these historically wandering tent-dwellers into the stability of permanent homes. Surprisingly, they have met with considerable success.

The creation of new settlements is not without problems, of

course. Sometimes they are bureaucratic, as in the instance of Neve Ilan, a proposed new town near Jerusalem backed by a group of Americans who want to take over an abandoned *kibbutz* and create a *moshav* based on a secondary school for emotionally disturbed children, an electronics workshop, and a Greenwich Village-style repertory theater and jazz workshop, along with a flower greenhouse and a mink farm. There was a good bit of backing and filling for a time between the Jewish Agency, which recognized Neve Ilan as a regular settlement eligible for government-provided housing, and the Housing Ministry, which said it was not an agricultural settlement and hence not eligible for such help. But the go-ahead has been given. At Yardena, a *moshav* settled by Kurdistani Jews from Iraq eighteen years ago, problems range from the fact that it is less than half a mile from Jordan to the fact that the settlers are far from modern and, for example, live without inside plumbing. Even the outside toilets have special problems, not the least of which is the necessity for armed guards watching for terrorist infiltrators.

All of the building that has taken place in Israel since 1948 has meant a lot of construction work. Although the nation is lacking in many basic resources, it is not lacking in manpower—traditionally, many new immigrants go right into heavy-duty work in building, public works, or agriculture—and it does have the stone and sand and ingredients for making bricks, glass, and cement. Israeli geologists have helped find large deposits of raw materials for building. The nation has been able to provide all the cement it needed and even export some, and it has also developed the technical capacity for manufacturing pipe and many of the other things that go into a house. The Israel Electric Company has kept up with the expansion (fortunately, Tabor came along with his solar heating units to provide hot water until cheap power was available everywhere), the development of the National Water Carrier and integrated water supply system has kept up with population growth, and the Technion's Building Research Center and other engineering laboratories have provided Israeli architects and construction men with technical advice and research about climatic effects on building materials and building design.

Until the first cement plant was built, local stone was used almost exclusively, and there was a variety of appearances as a result. Older Jerusalem buildings are of gray Mizzi jahudi or reddish-beige Mizzi ahmar quarried from the rock formations in the Judean hills. Haifa abounds in yellowish-gray Yabis and white Sultaneh; Safed and Nazareth show bright-colored Ka'akule stone in older buildings, while Tiberias and Beisan have many buildings made of dark basalt. Early post-State building in Eilat was largely with rock gypsum. However, the opening of highways, cement plants in Ramle and in the Negev, and the increased ability to transport stone and brick is bringing a sort of universal look to new developments, apartment houses, and other buildings, so that, with the exception of differences in size, terrain, and plant life, Kiryat Shmona in the north and Beersheba in the south are pretty much look-alikes, Upper Nazareth looks much like new parts of Jerusalem, and Tel Aviv is distinguished only by its size and its hodgepodge of architectural styles.

Israeli architecture is pretty much a mixed bag. After World War I, under the British Mandate, Palestinian architects concentrated more on copying Oriental forms than on adapting to local and climatic conditions. Subsequently, newer immigrant architects, educated in the 1920's and 1930's, starting building as they were taught in their native lands, with a European flavor. The first efforts to confront the climate were those of Kauffmann and of Zeev Rechter. Rechter designed the first house in Tel Aviv on pillars to allow air to pass between the ground floor and the hot soil—the prototype of what is still the most common apartment house design in Israel. Following World War II and the establishment of the State, building expanded rapidly and the housing problem was eventually solved. But, in the view of Professor Al Mansfield, of the Technion Faculty of Architecture and Town Planning, "the architectural quality of the settlements and buildings remained questionable." Architectural planning for new towns was "based on the garden suburb schemes imported from England and the rigid application of the 'neighborhood unit' principle," relying on "so-called standard building types" and not paying much attention to differing climates or landscape.

Mansfield is disappointed that the *kibbutz,* as a unique form of collective living, did not find expression in architecture. Far from evolving its own "visual image," the only way a *kibbutz* can usually be recognized from a distance, he says, is by its overextended agricultural buildings. The living quarters are generally small single houses, although there is some concentration of social functions in larger buildings.

A new generation of architects who came along in the 1950's have placed more emphasis on the sculptural aspect of building and strive for new space concepts and better integration of buildings into their environment, but, insists Mansfield, "Israel—despite her cosmopolitan character—is still a developing country and a small developing country at that. This means, among other things, that her industrialization is still in an early stage, forcing upon our architecture certain limitations." He points out that prefabricated building elements cannot yet be manufactured with high precision and says that, while the development of architecture the world over will certainly be strongly affected by the industrialization of the building process, Israeli architecture "is probably to retain its preponderantly artisan character, at least in the foreseeable future."

Israeli architecture has produced some striking construction—the big hotels, the Haifa Municipal Theater, and the Concert Hall in Tel Aviv, the highly imaginative design of new buildings on the various university campuses. Yet Ada Louise Huxtable, the architecture critic of *The New York Times*, described the esoteric-looking Bat Yam City Hall as "a remarkable flight of creative fancy grounded in poor execution and detail. It is a grand concept—including a combination ceremonial-emergency stair to a miniature amphitheater—that appears to have baffled a small town bureaucracy, which maintains the whole thing on the level of a kind of giant locker room."

There are good signs, nonetheless. Reconstruction in the Jewish quarter of the Old City of Jerusalem is adhering closely to the traditional design and size of the ages-old buildings that make up that colorful, historic section, and many new housing developments are designed so that rooms can be added as families grow, for overcrowding is a perennial problem and even most new apartments have fairly small rooms. And the Israeli building industry is meeting the challenge. In 1949, the country produced only 241,000 tons of cement; by 1964, the output passed 1 million tons. New techniques were developed, largely at the Technion's Building Research Center. Prefabricated concrete trusses eliminated the need for importing wood for concrete forms. (One of the hardest things for an American to get used to is seeing all those houses built without wood. The floors are generally cool ceramic tile or stone. Four factories for the prefabrication of entire houses are in operation, carrying forward the tradition started in the days of the overnight tower-and-stockade construction of the 1936–38 period. In addition, Israel trains more than 2,500 adults annually for the building trades.

Israeli scientists and engineers devote considerable attention today to the problems of the building industry. Professor Itzhak Alpan, Associate Professor at the Faculty of Civil Engineering at the Technion, is an expert on earthquake problems and soil mechanics. He has worked closely with construction people on foundation problems resulting from the tendency of many Israeli soils to swell. It is a problem that, he says, involves virtually the entire civil engineering faculty, whose members have devised a variety of techniques using protective shells, deep pits, membranes, and sleeving to meet individual situations. There are other problems, too, such as building in the collapsible loess soils or on the sandy dunes. Obviously, research in such areas also relates to building roads, airfields, and other construction.

Alpan was once called in as an expert on quarry-blasting and its effects on nearby housing, which led to a nationwide survey to set up guidelines and standards for quarry operators. He would like to tackle the problem of pile-driving vibration, but has not found the building industry quite that research minded.

Perhaps the best summary of how research advances building practice in Israel can be provided by Professor Rahel Shalon, head of the government's Building Research Station at the Technion—and probably the only woman in the world with such a job. "Along with basic research, building research in Israel covers studies of problems faced by the professions, by contractors, and by producers of materials and structural elements," she says. "A considerable part of our effort is devoted to selected problems stemming from local climatic and economic conditions and to investigation of materials and methods developed elsewhere with a view to adapting them to local circumstances."

The Israel Rural Building Research Center was founded in 1958, and its main focus is, of course, on rural building. However, it exists as part of the Technion Research and Development Foundation and deals with many basic construction problems. When the Center started functioning, relatively little was known about hot-climate building problems, but there were many indications of adverse climatic effects on concrete, and corrosion of steel reinforcing rods, for example. Because so much attention is being directed at development of the south, both laboratory and field studies have concentrated to a large extent on conditions in the semiarid northern Negev and the southern desert.

All this may not sound as exciting, perhaps, as bringing water to the thirsty and making a desert bloom to provide food for the masses, but housing and industrial construction are necessary to Israel's people. There is no more spectacular tragedy than the collapse of an apartment building in which families are living.

The Technion researchers have come up with a new technique for replacing traditional reinforced concrete elements by pre-stressing tendons to increase the resistance to pulls and pushes created by shifting subsoil or expansion of a roof slab, for instance, caused by the hot sun. They have also devised a way of predicting the buckling of elastically braced metal components, so proper allowances could be made. In the field of building climatology, they have devised methods for determining the physiological requirements of people living in Israel's various climates—such factors as good ventilation, reduction of indoor temperature during the day, or rapid cooling at night. They have studied the comfort factors of ceiling heights, window design and location, and a host of factors relating to buildings and their environment. Research on the way heat radiates from a building led to the construction of a prototype house in Eilat in which the combination of roof design (it was covered with polyethylene sheets), window location, and ceiling height created a built-in cooling pattern that reduced the indoor temperature by as much as 20°F. without recourse to expensive air conditioning or the use of desert coolers (a device that moves air over wet straw). The Israeli Meteorological Service also is involved in providing specific climatological data for each proposed development area, to help decide what crops, industries, and housing are appropriate.

If the work on cooling Negev houses alone pays off, it will mean a better life for people in the overheated southern part of the country, Israel's last frontier for large-scale population development.

Technion engineers are presently deeply involved in acoustical studies, to see what can be done to reduce noise in apartment houses and hospitals (if they solve the latter problem, they will earn the gratitude of unhappy patients the world over). They are seeking insulation to protect people from such aggravations as footsteps upstairs and the rush of running water through the walls. The feeling is that the climate is enough to bear without other irritations.

As a Jewish nation, Israel has a national interest in synagogues and religious tradition. So it seems appropriate to close this chapter with a word on synagogue design. At the same time that the oldest synagogue in the world, on the top of Masada, has been partially restored, and in Jerusalem Hebrew University archeologists are painstakingly uncovering the rest of the western wall—the Wailing Wall of Jewish history—of the Second Temple, a Technion architect has designed and built for that university a magnificently modern, but simple, synagogue. It bodes well for this great engineering school that faculty and students recognize that even in this fast-moving space age there is the necessity for technology to provide an appropriate House for the Lord.

X

In Defense of a People*

In the center of busy downtown Jerusalem, there is a statue of an odd-looking mortar called the *Davidka*. In the living room of a comfortable home in a Herzliya suburb there is another, smaller model of the *Davidka*, this one with a laser in the muzzle of the stubby barrel.

The *Davidka*—named after an ancient David who slew a well-armed Goliath—symbolizes the improvisational approach used by

* As inhabitants of a small nation surrounded by armies that have sworn their extinction, the Israelis are extremely security conscious. Correspondents in Israel are subject to military censorship. When picking up a hitch-hiking soldier, one doesn't ask, as in the United States, "Where are you stationed?" One day I was driving down a road when two Israeli Air Force fighter planes took off from a nearby field and roared over my car. My Israeli companion grinned at me and said, "Well, here we are, somewhere in Israel." At the time I was in Israel, the Israeli press was not allowed to write about certain warships built in Israeli shipyards, which tourists could see from their hotel windows and which were described by a *New York Times* correspondent in a story filed from outside Israel. For this chapter, I readily agreed to certain interviews on the interviewee's terms. It will not satisfy anyone looking for startling information on modern Israeli military technology. Rather, its purpose is to indicate the way improvisation and scientific ingenuity are applied to military matters vital to Israel's survival as they are to other necessities such as water supply and agriculture. For the information of the reader, this chapter of the book was voluntarily submitted to the Israel Defense Ministry for review.

the Israelis in applying science and technology to the defense of their people. Although the unusual weapon is in no way comparable to the modifications of French and American jet aircraft to meet the conditions of warfare in the Middle East, nor to the fast, computerized warships now manufactured in Israeli shipyards, it served its purpose magnificently during the War of Liberation.

The *Davidka* was the Haganah's answer to the cannons and heavy mortars used by the Arabs during the siege of Jerusalem. The defenders had virtually no heavy weapons, so the Haganah command asked scientists and technicians to produce some kind of gun that could reply effectively to the Arab artillery. This oddball mortar was designed by the late Eliahu Sochachever, then head of the Hebrew University's mechanical workshops. It looks much like the early round-barreled machine guns without their belts of bullets and its barrel is so narrow that only the tail-end of the shell could be inserted.

The barrels were made of hardened steel axles taken from locomotives in the 'Jerusalem railroad station, cut up and hollowed out with lathes. The shells were irrigation pipes filled with explosives made by Hebrew University chemists. It was used effectively around Jerusalem and with unique effectiveness at Safed in the Galilee, where its booming sound was followed by a sudden rainstorm. The Israelis spread the word that this strange weapon had introduced nuclear fallout into the rain. The Arab troops and villagers fled. Thus, the strategic scholarly Jewish community at Safed was rescued, thanks to a one-time locomotive axle that made a loud noise.

This kind of improvisation runs through what can be told of the science and technology of the Israeli military. It dates well back into the Haganah days before the State was proclaimed and continues up to today. For example, the Israeli Air Force, as modern as an air force can be, still has unique problems. It operates in a very small area, is relatively small in size, and needs a capability for quick landing, rearming, refueling, and turn-around takeoff. By modifying the rearming and reloading equipment on the ground and on the planes, the Israel Air Force managed a turn-around time of about nine minutes. A demonstration was arranged for military attachés of foreign embassies. Unimpressed, the assembled guests shrugged off the show of proficiency as play-acting.

Not long afterward, in the Six-Day War, the play-acting turned into reality. The fast-moving Israelis, flying sortie after sortie to put enemy air and tank forces out of action as swiftly as possible, brought the turn-around time for fighter bombers to just seven minutes.

Where and when the Jews in Palestine first began to use scientific ingenuity for military purposes is hard to say. Was it when Joshua undermined the walls of Jericho or when Samson raced two foxes with burning tails through an enemy village to frighten the superstitious foe away in the dead of night (a feat repeated many centuries later by Moshe Dayan's Eighth Brigade at Ramle in 1948, the only difference being that Dayan's modern foxes were flame-throwers tied to the back of a jeep that raced through the strategic crossroads town—the defenders fled without firing a shot).

For modern Israel, it began in the Haganah days of the 1930's. Before World War I, Jewish settlements in Palestine were defended by an organization known as *Hashomer*, The Watchmen. After the war, with anti-Jewish riots intensifying, the Haganah was formed to provide better-organized protection of Jewish lives against Arab attacks. This clandestine fighting force, which had its own secret workshops to make and service what few arms it had, existed until the State of Israel was proclaimed and it became the basis for the Israel Defense Forces.

The communications section of the Haganah in the Haifa area, for example, consisted of students at the Reali Technical High School, and many of the specially needed mines and explosives were made by engineers and scientists at the Technion in secret workshops. Some arms were manufactured in below-ground workshops at various *kibbutzim*, and munitions were made in secret rooms at a cannery where even the people in the next room did not know what was going on.

Former Prime Minister David Ben-Gurion, while chairman of the Jewish Agency Executive in the British Mandate days, arranged the purchase of arms, machine tools to make arms, and heavy equipment—much of which had to be smuggled into the country. He subsequently wrote an introduction to a book by Munya M. Mardor about the Haganah, in which he said:

> The methods and tactics of Haganah were unorthodox. They had to be. Customary ways and means were closed to us by the simple fact that Palestine was under the British Mandatory administration. We became grimly conscious, however, of the fact that our existence in the country as a people had become seriously threatened and that forces were gathering outside the boundaries of Palestine with the object of destroying us.

An early example of technical ingenuity utilized by the Haganah ordnance people was a reprisal attack after settlers in the fields of Ramat Yohanan had been waylaid by an armed Arab gang. The Haganah learned that the gang had retreated through the village of Sa'sa' and had stayed the night at the Mukhtar's house. Determined to set an example by blowing up the Mukhtar's home without harming anyone else, the Haganah developed a special mine, a conglomeration of wooden boxes filled with gelignite and a grease-gun-like apparatus that delayed the contact pin for three minutes while the night squad escaped. To develop limpet mines to attach to British gunboats blocking illegal immigrant ships, the Haganah used a workshop at the Shemen Edible Oil Factory, and first tried to hold the mines to the ships' hulls with magnets from telephone equipment. They proved too weak, so the jerry-built mines had to wait until stronger magnets could be smuggled into Haifa. On another occasion, the Haganah blew up a section of the Iraq Oil pipeline with an unusual crescent-shaped mine designed to fit the curve of the pipe and filled with explosives made in a Haganah laboratory.

In 1947, as the situation grew tense with the nearing of the end of the British Mandate, arms were urgently needed. They were smuggled into Haifa in dummy machinery built with concealed chambers at a farm near Milan. The weapons, which included Bren and Sten guns, were dismantled at the farm and packed into every nook and cranny of the machinery.

So desperate were the Israelis for weapons and planes in 1948 that even one enemy Spitfire that was shot down was recovered from the Mediterranean and reconditioned. Munya Mardor, who was then involved in clandestine operations in Europe, where he was seeking armaments by all and any means, tells how the Haganah forces sank a ship in Bari, Italy, which was carrying arms to the Arabs.

First, explosives were smuggled into Bari in a dummy American Army truck with a spare fuel tank in which the explosives and equipment were hidden. The tank was labeled "DDT—Extermination of Vermin," and was topped off by a little pump that would actually produce DDT for any curious official. The mine used to sink the ship was assembled, not in a workshop, but in a hotel room. There were bottles of sulphuric acid all over the place, turned upside down with their mouths stuffed with varying thicknesses of newsprint. Beneath each bottle was a heap of potash. This was the only way the Haganah people could check the time it took for the acid to eat through, so they could tell how long it would take for the mine's fuse to be activated. Lacking other laboratory equipment, they improvised to find out how much time the frogmen would have to escape after attaching the mines to the munitions ship. The casing of the mine was the inner tube of a motorcycle tire, filled with TNT. The detonators were covered by rubber contraceptives to protect them from the water. When the time came, one of the bottles was fitted to an inner tube. The strange contraption was attached to the side of the ship, the acid flowed down to the potash, created enough heat to explode the TNT, and there went a load of Arab ammunition.

More than two decades afterward, Mardor, who has spent a good part of his life in the Haganah and in weapons-development research for the Israel Defense Forces (IDF), lives comfortably in a small town near Herzliya. He can sit on a screened-in veranda drinking *butz* coffee and watching his dog frolic on the lawn, but he is never very far from the grim realities with which he and his scientific associates must deal.

In his living room is a half-sized model of the *Davidka*, presented to him by his anonymous associates for twenty years of research service for the IDF. The laser ruby in the muzzle is symbolic of advances in weaponry. It does not (I repeat, does not) indicate that the Israelis are using the laser as a weapon.

Before the War of Liberation, the Haganah scientists concentrated largely on making special mines and limpets in the struggle to circumvent British curbs on immigration. "Our engineers developed special kinds for each operation," he says. "They were primitive but complex enough for complicated conditions. In 1939, during the time of the British White Paper against the aliyah, the Technion professors were our 'Engineer Corps.'" So clandestine were these engineers that one, Jenka Ratner, who later headed IDF scientific research, was taken to England to work on antisubmarine devices in World War II. The British never knew that he had helped design the limpet mines used against their patrol craft.

The first weapon actually assembled in Palestine was the Sten gun, made at first from parts smuggled in by Mardor's groups in Europe and assembled in an underground workshop at a *kibbutz* near Haifa. Subsequently, the Haganah workshops also developed the *Davidka* and began producing two- and three-inch mortars. The Haganah munitions industry was called Ta'as, and it has become Israel's national armaments industry.

Although it now has a capability for producing everything from the nasty-looking Uzzi, a short-barreled but extremely effective submachine gun, medium-sized cannon, and a variety of other weapons, to replacement parts for tanks and jeeps, shells and rocket propellants, and jet aircraft engines and spare parts for planes, Ta'as managed to remain virtually a secret operation until last year, when a motion picture on its work was distributed to Israeli theaters. Even though Ta'as uses the most modern electronic equipment, it is still using the original presses bought in America as scrap iron in the underground days.

Another key figure in military research and development was Professor Ernst David Bergmann, who is back teaching organic chemistry full time at the Hebrew University after serving eighteen years as head of Scientific Research and Development for the Ministry of Defense. Bergmann looks like an Israeli version of Robert Donat playing Mr. Chips in a chemistry lab. But his memories are far from Chips-like.

Besides Bergmann, many others at the university have been and are involved in defense-related research, and many of the faculty and students at the Technion are or will be similarly involved. Bergmann and Mardor are two who are known for their work; most scientists and engineers in defense research are anonymous, even though much of their work may eventually have civilian application. Their neighbors do not know what they do, they do not publish, they do not talk about their activities. There is always the danger that they might some day be captured and that, if they were known for their defense research, be tortured for information. The borders are close enough to make kidnapping possible.

Before going into some of Bergmann's experiences, it might be well to say something about the relationship of Israeli scientists to defense work, for this almost universal willingness to play a part in the nation's defense establishment may startle and disturb many Americans who sympathize with student demonstrations against defense research on their campuses and who picket Dow Chemical and military recruiters.

One does not get the feeling that these Israeli scientists are blood-thirsty, militaristic, or violent. What does come through, again, is the feeling of *ein breira*. No alternative. They are in Israel because they believe in a Jewish homeland and nation. They have deep feelings that they are the ones who some day may have to prevent another holocaust like that which saw 6 million Jews exterminated by the Nazis. They would rather live in peace, but they do not really believe that anyone but themselves can or will protect the semblance of peace in which they now live. (I heard one young, extremely skilled radar analyst in the Israel Air Force say with great vehemence, "I hate Arabs because they forced me to learn to kill.") They watch Israeli jets heading for the Suez or the Jordanian border and their reaction is not militaristic; rather, it is a short prayer that the pilots will return safely. They know that their best defense is to use their technical and scientific ingenuity to give their small fighting forces the best possible chance when the chips are down.

When the British left Palestine on May 14, 1948, and the State was proclaimed, Israel was invaded by six well-equipped Arab armies. The Arabs had tanks, jets, armored cars, artillery, warships, and plenty of ammunition. The Jewish defenders consisted of 3,000 Palmach soldiers, 9,500 in the special Haganah field units, and about 35,000 Haganah people trained for limited local defense. They had 2,500 foreign volunteers, largely airmen or naval personal, and a total of 10,000 rifles of all makes, 3,600 submachine guns (mostly the illegally-made Stens), about 900 machine guns, 800 small mortars, 19 antitank rifles, some grenades, explosives, and homemade Molotov cocktails. With this, they managed to hold off the invaders at many points and gradually push them back in others. The jeep light-armored charge was their major military tactic.

Bergmann recalls that the people were so unskilled in warfare that, when guns were dropped from their few aircraft to one beleaguered *kibbutz*, the *kibbutzniks* radioed back that they didn't know how to use them and instructions had to be radioed to the people on the ground.

The few 65mm guns they were able to buy from the French were mounted on railcars and taken directly to the front. Mardor says they were "just junk, but they were our best artillery." Trucks were steel plated for use in lieu of tanks. The only suitable raw material for ammunition was potash; Hebrew University chemists swiftly turned to devising new methods of turning it into gunpowder and explosives.

All this had to be done hastily. Bergmann comments that military research in Israel had begun on the level of "hobbies" rather than basic knowledge. The creation of the State was not evolutionary, but swift, and left no time for transitional development. The British had done everything possible to inhibit a military industry in Palestine and had put strict limits on the importation of nitric acid, without which one can't make explosives or chemical propellants. But the Israelis found a way. They did have ample supplies of nitrogenous fertilizers from which nitrates could be extracted and a supply of sulphuric acid. By heating the nitrates with sulphuric acid, they were able to make their own nitric acid. A plant was set up overnight to do this, which Bergmann calls "a most idiotic thing," for it reversed the normal industrial process, taking nitric acid out of nitrates instead of making the nitrates out of the acid. He adds quietly that the production of nitric acid out of nitrates is not economically sound, but somehow the question didn't arise at the time. There was not enough nitric acid available even then to make both explosives and propellants, so mining explosives were used for military purposes. Another plant was swiftly set up to make potassium chlorate for explosives out of available potash.

"At the time, we were willing to take anything," he says, "but it was not an optimal solution. If you need an industry to make propellants, you need one with a capacity for making propellants not only for common or mortar shells but also for rockets."

The Israelis learned that the United States had a propellant that could be made from potash. Working from partial information in semitechnical journals, the Israelis became the second nation in the world to use the process, which led them to a long-term research and development program. Today, they can produce rocket propellants comparable to those of other countries and could, if they wanted to, produce enough to put a satellite in orbit.

During the War of Independence, the actual manufacture of munitions was done in army workshops, but the delicate detonators were turned out at Hebrew University. It was not unusual for a scientist to get a phone call in the evening saying, "Where in hell are those detonators we asked for this morning? We need them within an hour."

The intense knowledge of the area gained by Israeli geologists, biologists, and others exploring Palestine has also paid off in many ways. Late in the War of Independence, an Egyptian brigade at Auja in the Negev was surprised by Israeli forces using a long-forgotten Roman road. Rapid advances through the Sinai in 1956 and 1967 were enhanced by intensive training exercises based on exact knowledge of the peninsula.

Little information was available about more recent developments in military technology until recently, although it was known that the Israelis had done remarkable things with Russian, British, and American equipment they captured during the Six-Day War or purchased from the United States or Great Britain. Much of the captured equipment was modified extensively for desert warfare and sent right back into action. Research on captured Russian SAM II missiles has, it is believed, led to the virtual neutralization of the ground-to-air weapon and may be one reason why the Russians are replacing them in Egypt with SAM III's. It may be assumed that recently captured Russian units will similarly pay off in knowledge of how to jam or evade radar.

On Independence Day in May, 1970, the Israelis took the secrecy lid off some of their accomplishments in military technology, unveiling officially the new Sa'ar class missile boats, which have been the subject of rumors and unconfirmed reports for about a year, the extensively modified Patton tank, and a new antitank gun mounted on a half-track.

The existence of the new Israeli missile boats was first reported by an American newspaper about a year before they were formally unveiled, but the story was never confirmed even though Israeli newsmen were allowed to see the ships at the time. When the Israelis blithely sailed six more of them out of Cherbourg in spite of the French embargo on arms to Israel, the secret began to leak out.

The sleek Sa'ar—on which conventional guns and gun mounts are replaced by squat boxes whose mouths open up, hippopotamuslike, to reveal the nose tips of Israel-made surface-to-surface Gabriel missiles inside—is one of the fastest and most sophisticated naval vessels in the Mediterranean. It can be used to seek out and destroy enemy ships and submarines, for coastal defense, and in support of the Army and Air Force. The ship is about 135 feet long, can travel faster than forty knots an hour, and carries eight electronically guided Gabriels and the most modern computerized radar and sonar equipment. The small vessel carries the punch of a battleship and is one of the most versatile warships afloat. Its small size makes detection difficult, and its speed makes it hard to hit. The Gabriel missile is another outstanding accomplishment of Israeli military technology and may well become an export item. Development of this over-the-horizon missile with its 150-kilo warhead took almost ten years; just two of them can sink a destroyer.

The Patton M-48 Mark A-3 tank represents improvisation upon the original vehicle, with diesel engines and British guns replacing the American equipment and unusually large fuel tanks enabling it to operate for ten hours without refueling, a marked advantage since the tank can fight all day and then be refueled and rearmed under the cover of darkness when tell-tale dust clouds will not indicate the movement of tankers and trucks bringing fuel and shells. The new version of the standard Patton is believed to be far superior to any Russian tanks the Egyptians have. Mounting the 90mm antitank gun on a half-track is another typical Israel improvisation and makes the weapon much more versatile for defense purposes than it was when it was a "sitting duck" installed in one position. The Bar Lev Line itself is reported to be a masterpiece of construction, based partially on improvisational use of tracks and ties from a railroad that ran along the Suez Canal.

The Israeli Air Force also had improvisational beginnings, starting with the Palmach gliding clubs in 1937 and carrying out weird air raids with a few beat-up Dakotas and other planes flown in by a dummy Panamanian line for the War of Independence. Until the first Messerschmitts were obtained from Czechoslovakia and flown to Israel, unassembled, in cargo planes, the only fighters Israel had were Piper Cubs and the one captured Spitfire.

Mardor was the first commandant of the fledgling Israel Air Transport Command. Years later, he said, "How we managed, and the devices we resorted to, would horrify any normal air force command. Talking it over now, it sometimes horrifies me. The whole air force was expanding, not organically but in leaps and bounds, and not with any prescribed pattern of aircraft but with anything it could lay its hands on. That, of course, brought about serious equipment problems, which, at least, in the case of my Air Transport Command, compelled one to take unconventional and extreme measures."

Unconventional is hardly the word for it. On one 1948 bombing effort, ladders were used for bomb racks and the bombs pushed out by hand.

Today, even though Israel has an aircraft industry that manufactures jet trainers and other planes suitable for either civilian or military purposes, great ingenuity is used to make spare parts or quickly repair damaged parts. Israel cannot afford to throw away damaged equipment, so the spirit of make-do still prevails.

Very little is known publicly about Israeli nuclear weapons research. The Israelis have admitted, according to Wesley Pruden,

Jr., of the *National Observer*, that their reactor at Dimona could produce enough plutonium for one Hiroshima-sized bomb each year, and they can extract uranium from Dead Sea phosphates. So far as is known, they do not have the kind of expensive automated plant required for making plutonium. And Israel is a signatory to the nuclear test–ban treaty.

In his book *Military and Politics in Israel* (Frank Cass and Co., Ltd., London, 1969) Amos Perlmutter, a former member of the Israel Atomic Energy Commission, has this to say:

> In Israel, science has always been closely tied to security. As early as 1947, the Haganah organized Hemed (scientific branch of Zahal, the military) which enlisted Israel's best scientists. The scientific army was inherited by Zahal, but has since been incorporated into the Ministry of Defense. In this manner, the production of nuclear weapons has been separated from the military proper. In the area of nuclear technology and the application of atomic and nuclear energy to both peaceful and military uses, the Defense Ministry is the supreme authority. Israel's nuclear reactors and missile factories are subject to the Ministry's control and supervision.

Because this is one of the few public statements on the subject of nuclear weapons ever made by an Israeli official, it might be noted that, elsewhere in his book, Perlmutter says that, under the guidance of former Defense Minister Shimon Peres the Defense Ministry "forged ahead on nuclear research and development," that one of Ben-Gurion's tasks between 1955 and 1960 was "to expand the Ministry's scientific and armament industries and develop a nuclear capability in Israel in the hope of eventually deterring the growing Arab military forces," and that later, when Levi Eshkol was Finance Minister, he cut the budget for such development.

According to the most recent issue of *Janes' All Aircraft*, Israel should have achieved production of nuclear warheads by 1970. Almost a full page in the missile section of the book is devoted to Israel, with the Gabriel and another intermediate-range surface-to-surface missile, the MD-660, both attributed to the Israel Defense Forces.

Describing the MD-660, *Janes'* says it can use either conventional or nuclear warheads, then adds: "It is suggested that Israel will have suitable nuclear warheads of its own design available in 1970—produced in the Dimona reactor and nuclear center near the Dead Sea."

These statements do not necessarily mean that Israel does have a nuclear weapons capability, for the military has been in the forefront of all kinds of civilian research and development in Israel, and even today—as indicated elsewhere—young soldiers in the *Nahal* outposts are doing research in farming and irrigation and others are cooperating with Steinitz' fish-migration study along the Suez, when circumstances permit. Yet, from the point of view of necessity, one can also deduce that some kind of nuclear capability probably does exist, because Israel is surrounded by increasingly sophisticated armies.

In August, 1968, Defense Minister Moshe Dayan wrote for the yearbook of the American Technion Society:

> As the Minister responsible for defense, I am concerned that our soldiers, airmen and sailors be trained to fight with courage, skill and ingenuity; that they be armed with the most modern weapons; and that they employ the most advanced technological systems. We shall always be outnumbered by our enemies in the neighboring states. We must continue to cover this numerical gap—as we did during the Six-Day War—by quality: superior fighting spirit and fighting proficiency. But we must ensure a similar superiority in technological standards.

The Technion campus that exists today was initiated by General Yacov Dori, the first Israeli commander in chief, when he became president of the Technion some years ago. It is built on ground that once was used for secret Haganah training purposes, just as the beautiful gardens near the Hebrew University campus on Mount Scopus once hid ammunition. Thus, it is obvious that the Israelis know how to beat their swords into plowshares, so to speak. But it is obvious, too, that they know how to beat their scientific plowshares into swords when they need to.

XI

The Technology of Ein Breira *and the* Years Ahead

David Vofsi and Al Schwimmer are the kind of men on whom the future of Israeli science and technology, and the country's economic viability, may well depend.

Vofsi, a Latvian who has been in Israel since 1938, is the head of the Plastics Research Laboratory at the Weizmann Institute. Schwimmer is an American businessman with a thriving aircraft-servicing firm in California. Their contributions to the industrialization of the country are important examples of how the technology of *ein breira* is changing its direction.

Vofsi's contribution is a pale synthetic plastic fluid that looks like diluted milk and is used to coat vegetables and fruits before they are exported to overseas markets. This polyethylene compound is a remarkable preservative. It extends the shelf-life of produce to phenomenal time spans (a coated grapefruit, kept for eight months at close to room temperature and six more in cold storage, was sampled by the U.S. Ambassador, who when he tasted the fruit said that he could hardly believe it had been around that long). Use of the solution greatly reduces the cost of shipping produce to market by making it possible to ship by boat instead of plane. It also eliminates the need to hand wrap each orange or other fruit or vegetable in paper as a protection against infestation.

A short, reddish-haired man who favors open-necked blue sport shirts, Vofsi has a pin-up collection of color photographs of fruits and vegetables that have or have not been treated with his chemical. The former would delight the heart of any food-shopping housewife, while the latter would cause her to change vegetable markets. But, like most Israeli scientists, Vofsi is not prone to dwell on what has been done. After displaying his wares, his talk turns to polyethylene plastic sheeting, widely used for greenhouses, packing, and many other purposes. "It's piling up all over the place. It never deteriorates, and it's clogging up the sewers."

Nobody in Israel is working on the problem, he laments, but he has an idea—development of plastic materials that can be eaten after they are used to package foods. Since most plastics presently in use have a petroleum base, this may mean working with botanists to develop plant oils that can be substituted for the petroleum.

An important aspect of Vofsi's successful project is that the solution is manufactured in an Israeli chemical plant in Beersheba, which means that his esoteric chemical laboratory has created jobs for Israelis as well as increased the profitability of citrus and other exports and has developed an export market for the solution itself. An American firm is experimenting with it in connection with the control of evapotranspiration of moisture from plant leaves.

Some people at the Weizmann Institute today question the "intrusion" of commercially oriented applied science into an institution of higher learning that focuses largely on basic research and education. They seem to forget or are ignoring the Institute's history, the work that Weizmann mathematicians and nuclear researchers have done in connection with oil- and water-exploration, the work in agricultural research by Weizmann biogeneticists, the Institute's support of the Defense Ministry, and, most of all, Chaim Weizmann's own statement that his experiments were designed to help the absorption of Jews returning to their homeland.

Al Schwimmer is not an Israeli, but his part in Israel's growth and development will some day be part of the nation's technological folklore. Schwimmer was one of the *marhal*—the America, British, Canadian, South African, and other volunteers who came to Israel in 1947 and 1948 to fight in the War of Independence. A former U.S. Air Force flight engineer, Schwimmer was part of Israel's fledgling Air Force in the grim days when even a Piper Cub was a combat plane. Afterward, he went back to Burbank and became a partner in a lucrative aircraft maintenance firm. In 1951, Prime Minister Ben-Gurion looked him up to suggest that Schwimmer set up an aircraft business in Israel. A lot of people were skeptical about the whole idea, but Schwimmer pointed out there wasn't a good maintenance setup between Italy and India. The Bedek Company—also known as Israel Aircraft Industries—was established in 1953 with an investment of less than $200,000 and only seventy employees. Today, it has well over 9,000 workers and is Israel's largest single industrial complex.

The company's original charter called for provision of essential aviation services, development of trained manpower, and export services. The first mechanics were local talent and some of the *marhal* people who had stayed on in Israel. As the company grew, it developed a capacity for making and designing spare parts and, in 1960, began producing the Fouga Magister jet trainer under a French license. The Magister ever since has been an integral part of the Israel Air Force.

An electronic subsidiary began producing avionics equipment, and even branched off into medical electronics. A few years later, Bedek began to design its own plane for the first time, and is now preparing to market a twenty-two–passenger STOL air taxi, the Arava, completely designed in Israel. The plane can be used for air ambulance work, agricultural spraying, supply drops, troop or paratroop transport, fire-fighting, bush and Alpine operation, and for transporting vehicles. Bedek also manufactures the small Jet Commander under license from an American firm.

Creation of an Israeli aviation industry was an absolute necessity. Israel cannot afford to be perpetually dependent upon outside sources for planes and parts. At first, the biggest problem at Bedek was a lack of skilled personnel; much of the work was on an improvisational basis. The story of how Schwimmer found three beat-up stratocruisers in a U.S. Air Force surplus boneyard and got three devil-may-care pilots to nurse them across the Atlantic to Israel has become a saga of modern aviation. But, once they arrived at Lod and major modifications were made by ingenious technicians, the planes became important rear-loading military cargo planes.

When the Arava was test flown and made its maiden flight in April, 1970, Bedek's chief test pilot, Captain Avraham Hacohen, put it through take-offs and landings requiring less than 360 yards and flew it over the field on one engine at only fifty-five knots, well below the stalling speed for the average plane. Impressive as his feat was, what Israeli Prime Minister Golda Meir had to say to the assembled aircraft workers was even more so.

"You are no longer dependent on others. We can stand alone even through a long, hard struggle," Mrs. Meir told them. She did not elaborate, but it is generally known that Israeli intelligence had managed to obtain the blueprints for the parts of the French jets the country is now flying. Al Schwimmer answered a press conference question, about whether or not Israel is building its own fighter plane, with the oblique statement, "We have the capability to make whatever the government may ask of us."

Over and beyond the manufacture of aircraft, Bedek helped create a whole new field of engineering specialization in Israel, with the Technion playing a major role in research and training. When the Aeronautical Faculty was created at Technion, there were objections that Technion would be turning out forty to fifty engineering specialists each year for whom there would be no jobs; they would leave for other countries and Israel would lose their talents. Just the opposite happened. Hundreds of Technion engineers are working for Bedek or its subsidiaries, and twice as many could be used. The aviation industry offers good job opportunities for new immigrants as well as for young Israeli engineers working in other countries. In addition, as indicated in other chapters, the aviation faculty has made important contributions in other areas of vitally needed technology from desalination to fruit-spraying.

These two examples highlight what is happening in Israel today. With agricultural development near its peak (for there will just not be enough water for a great deal of expansion of farming in the years ahead) and with the population still growing, there is a need for industry to create jobs. Science-based industry, with a large return for initial investment in raw materials and labor, is the most economically sensible answer for the future.

But, at the same time, there are increasing problems finding money for scientific and engineering research, and the jobs of perhaps 1,400 scientists and engineers literally depend upon the future funding of their efforts by new sources such as science-based industry or Israeli Government research aimed at industrial development.

In a report to the American Technion Society in 1968, Professor Moshe Arens, Chief Engineer for Israel Aircraft Industries, said, "Israel is an industrial entity. Its economic viability will depend to no small measure on its technical achievements and its ability to translate engineering and scientific skills into the commercial and defense products required by the nation."

Approximately one-third of the research financing in the recent past has come from abroad—much of that over-all figure from U.S. Government agencies, although dependency upon U.S. Government funding varies considerably from project to project. The Hebrew University's authority for Research and Development signed 182 new research contracts and extended forty-four more in fiscal 1968–69. Approximately 70 per cent of the dollar value of these 226 contracts is represented by the seventy-three that are underwritten by U.S. federal agencies.

U.S. Government money, however, will not be available much beyond 1973, for the funds used have been largely counterpart Israeli currency used to purchase U.S. surplus commodities under Public Law 480. The PL-480 funds in Israel are drying up quickly, especially since Israel is not using much in the way of surplus food commodities from the United States any more. At the same time, budgetary restrictions in Washington are sharply reducing funds for all overseas research activities. The greatest reductions are in the agricultural field, which presents a particular problem for the Hebrew University's School of Agriculture. The Weizmann Institute, too, is hurting because of projected reductions in U.S. overseas health research.

Negotiations between the Israel Embassy in Washington and the U.S. Government were instrumental in extending current research funding to 1973, but Israel is moving as quickly as possible to change its basic source of funding. The main focus is on industrial research and development. Each of the three major universities has a research and development subsidiary already tied into newly created science-based industries and is seeking other research areas that can turn out products or services that can be manufactured in Israel.

The Weizmann Institute has the Yeda Research and Development Company, Ltd., which, since 1959, has processed over 425 patent applications, of which 190 already have matured into patents in various countries. Yeda also puts potential sponsors of industrial research in touch with scientists concerned with industrial problems. In 1969, as a result of this effort, Weizmann projects were being sponsored by Monsanto, Diamond Shamrock Corporation, and Kalvex, Inc., of the United States; Interlab S/A, of Switzerland; Robert Bosch, of West Germany; and Makhteshim, Ltd., Abic, Ltd., and Agan Chemicals Ltd., of Israel. The Hebrew University has Yissum Research Development Company, formed in 1964, which has already been involved in the creation of three science-based industries in Jerusalem: Ames-Yissum, Ltd., a joint company with Miles Laboratories that makes and sells diagnostic systems developed at the university; Makor Chemicals, manufacturer of biological compounds, enzymes, and fermentation products; and Elron Electronic Industries, which makes a solid-state gamma-ray detector in the university's physics workshop. The Technion Research and Development Foundation, Ltd., has, since its founding in 1953, carried out more than 900 different industrial research projects.

In just a few months in early 1970, the ingenuity and inventiveness of Israeli scientists and engineers have created a variety of new products on which science-based industries or new factories can be developed. Among them are a simple classroom teaching aid system that costs about $86.00 per pupil; a new and relatively inexpensive device for inducing laser beams in metal tubes instead of glass; a mechanical ladder for fruit-picking, which is already being sold to American ranchers; and a new heavy water concentrate. A publisher of scientific translations has become the country's leading publishing house. Of the sixty-three projects for investment in Israel developed by an economic conference in the United States during 1969, sixteen involved science-based industries, fourteen were in metals, eleven in chemicals and foods, five in textiles and leather. Only seventeen could not be in some way related to technology, scientific or agricultural.

The annual economic conferences also work at creating a reverse brain drain, which will bring Israeli scientists and engineers back to their country and, in 1969, contributed to the return of some 800 Israeli professionals, 300 of them in the aircraft industry alone. A report to the Finance Ministry recently indicated that Israel will need to double the number of engineers in 1975 and treble it by 1980, with 40 per cent of this increase in the machinery, electronics, and automotive industries alone. The report says that Israeli universities must double their output of engineers and that lower schools must be improved to provide qualified university students.

Against this background, Eliazer Tal, Director of the National Council for Research and Development, is fairly sanguine about what the future holds. He recognizes that some 1,400 professional jobs are currently hanging on U.S. funding and that alternative sources will have to be found to prevent a possible brain drain when the U.S. money is gone. But rapid industrialization and industrial investment and funds from other sources, such as the United Nations Food and Agricultural Organization, which is funding a program to improve vegetable and flower production in Israel, have already become part of the answer. His thinking is that alternatives might include: (1) contracts with firms doing applied research (Israeli scientific standards are high and salaries are low, so investors get a lot of high quality research for their money), (2) Israeli Government projects (but this will mean that many scientists may have to switch fields to make up for shortages of skilled researchers in areas of specific importance to the government—a biologist might move over to pharmacology; a physicist, to electronics; or a microbiologist, to fermentation), and (3) an Israeli Government move into some fields of basic research.

"This will give the government a good opportunity to change the mood of Israeli science from one of basic research to one of applied research aimed at the long-term improvement of the economy," he says. "Government support will just have to keep expanding, if there are to be jobs for new graduates until new science-based industries can grow and absorb the men and women coming out of the institutions of higher learning. In the physical sciences and engineering, there is no problem, but the life sciences will have to adapt to changed circumstances."

Tal believes that the traditions of Israeli science will prevail with most of the people involved, that the time-honored Jewish respect for learning has been transferred to some extent from the rabbi to the scientist, and that the legacy of the Zionist movement still creates a feeling of pioneering in most Israel scientists and engineers. Low Israeli salaries are no real problem, so far as he can see, for again the nation's spirit is overriding. At times, Tal says, he has difficulty finding people to take overseas assignments at higher incomes, and every report on the effects of the brain drain caused by the early 1967 depression indicates that the surge of economic activity following the Six-Day War has brought back to Israel a steady stream of professionals who had been working outside the country or studying abroad.

There are, he believes, now plenty of career opportunities arising from the absorption of new technologies and from management of industrial problems—quality control of water, air pollution control, even traffic control. Also, there are many opportunities in Israeli overseas technical programs. Tahal has water- and other resource-development programs going on in many parts of the world. Dan Goldberg, the Hebrew University's trickle irrigation expert, traveled to South Korea on an irrigation development assignment. Israelis are involved, too, in many U.N. development programs around the world.

Israeli technical-assistance activities are highly successful, and large numbers of foreign students, especially from Africa, study at Israeli colleges and universities. Herman Finkle, a gray-haired Middle Western American agricultural engineer who supervises technical-assistance programs in his field at the Technion, notes that Technion has already graduated 110 students from 25 countries with degrees in agricultural engineering.

He tells of an American engineer who went to Africa to evaluate U.S. programs there and who finally came to Israel because wherever he went in Africa he kept running into Israeli technical assistance. Said the engineer, "Wherever I went, the American expert was assumed likely to fail unless he worked hard enough to succeed, whereas the Israelis were assumed likely to succeed unless they were goof-offs. I want to know why people feel this way."

Finkle offers some answers, which may also serve to explain why so many technical developments succeed so swiftly in Israel, too.

First, Israeli technical-assistance programs get under way much faster than American programs. This is a result of small-scale lines of communication. For example, when Tahal got a call from the Thai Foreign Ministry requesting an evaluation of a big irrigation project on a Wednesday, Tahal engineers were in Thailand the following Monday.

Second, almost all Israelis are used to working in the field. At home, they spend a great deal of their time in field-level operations or research. Their personal requirements are based on life in an austere country. They are willing to eat local food, and also, says Finkle, have the Jewish gift for languages.

Moreover, they are given enormous leeway in devising their own programs without having to get home office clearance. This kind of experience and training pays off when you're doing a job on someone else's territory. Experience with improvisation also pays off. "If you come from a country with first-rate equipment, you're lost in a developing country," Finkle says. "But, if you come from a country that knows what good equipment is, but also knows how to make do without it, you're ahead of the game." He recalls one project in southern Iran in which the immediate goal was to get a farm running on 86,000 acres of land. "If we'd waited for equipment, we'd never have done it. We didn't wait. We just improvised with whatever we could lay our hands on."

Also, he adds, experts from large countries talk too much about the way they do things back home. An expert from a small country like Israel is more likely to create an atmosphere in which people in another small country have confidence in their own abilities.

Thinking small, in effect, is one of the hopes of the science-based-industry approach to the future. Israel cannot afford to build big plants to compete in the open market with large industrial nations. The Israeli tire factory, for instance, makes mostly odd-sized special-order tires with which large assembly-line plants don't want to bother. Israel is now negotiating with a lot of firms and foundations for the establishment of plants in the country. Such organizations as the Volkswagen Foundation and the Nestlé Foundation are interested. Fund-raising specialists are canvasing the world for sources of research support.

The country has a large vocational-training program at the high school level, to create technicians for existing and new industries, many of which are operated by *kibbutzim* or *moshavem*. Also, the Weizmann Institute has an annual summer science camp to encourage future researchers and, along with the other universities, is deeply involved in improving science education at the high school level. (Even so, Israel is busy recruiting immigrant technical specialists in many fields to staff the new science-based industries. Necessity is still the governing factor—there is just not enough time to wait for the educational process to run its course.)

All these considerations hold many implications for social changes in Israel. The young *kibbutznik*, for example, is harder and harder to keep on the farm now that so many technological careers are being offered. And the recruitment effort aimed at bringing more specialists to Israel holds out the possibility of shortcuts and extra privileges that have not in the past been offered to immigrants.

It all comes down to the essential premise, *ein breira*. Israel continues to have no alternative. It needs more science and technology, just as did the first settlers in the 1890's and the early 1900's. If peace comes to the Middle East, Israeli expertise can be shared with the whole troubled area. Even now, Israeli agricultural experts are helping Arab farmers in the occupied territories, in the Gaza Strip, and in Samaria, to utilize modern farming methods that have vastly increased their output and their incomes. The technology of *ein breira* that helped build a nation, given a chance, can also be of great assistance to Israel's immediate neighbors and their peoples, just as it already has been in other parts of Africa and in Latin America.

Meanwhile, the feeling of national pride and pioneering, which still prevails, keeps Israeli science and technology high in quality and unique in spirit. Laborers in a Dead Sea bromine plant rush out to greet an old physical chemist when he makes an infrequent visit. A young engineer sweating in the sun looks for a sponge rubber ball lost in a maze of tubing—and knows that he is contributing to national survival. So does a pretty brunette from New York, as she works hard trying to grow something so small she can't even see it just to feed a gray mullet. Not even the venerable old-timers like Leo Picard or Rudy Bloch seem to be resting on their laurels, and one gets the feeling that, as soon as Israel Libertovsky builds his first supertanker, he'll be rushing off to some entirely new field.

The same technological tenacity that hewed a water-supply conduit into the rock under the old city of Jerusalem 2,500 years ago is still in evidence today, making its own computers and laser rubies, getting ready to desalt the sea, and, in a plant near Nazareth, assembling a fiber glass–bodied car called the Susita (it is also called the "camel car," because camels have been known to chew on the fiber glass). Lush farms that once were swamps, a fantastic national water system, a desert *kibbutz* where cows give more milk than anyone has a right to expect, a factory in the middle of nowhere producing the newest kind of fertilizer from natural resources that were overlooked for centuries, a statue of a crazy weapon made out of locomotive axles —remind the world that even the most sophisticated science and technology can be improved by a good leavening of improvisation.

Index